PRAISE FOR FELICE COHEN'S

HALF IN: A COMING-OF-AGE MEMOIR OF FORBIDDEN LOVE

"*Half In* is ever tempting. But the only way to live is all in, pedal to the metal. Felice Cohen's journey is full of potholes, bumps, sharp curves but she makes it home."

—Rita Mae Brown, author of Rubyfruit Jungle

"Filled with the exquisite joy of new love, and the pain of walking away from it, *Half In* is an intimate memoir about growth toward self-awareness—and toward the poignant realization that love calls for a wholehearted commitment."

—Foreword Reviews

"Felice keeps it real in *Half In*. She shares her struggles. She shares her thoughts. She shares her truth. She shares her journey of maturity. She does it in an entertaining light that most readers will come to appreciate."

—Reader Views

"Felice Cohen shares her story without holding back any facts and details and that helps readers understand how the affair shaped her and how the repercussions affected her daily life."

—Readers' Favorite

"I could not put this memoir down. Felice Cohen walks us through her experience of first love—a relationship that could easily be labeled as scandalous—with honesty, humor, and insight. It is as if she is cracking open an old diary and inviting us inside. Meeting Felice through *Half In* is like making a new friend."

—Jodi S. Rosenfeld, author of Closer to Fine

"Filled with sparkling conversations and haunting encounters, this page-turner seeks to enlighten as well as pay tribute to a once in a lifetime love."

—Booklife

"*Half In* is a top recommendation not just for LGBTQ collections, but any library strong in either coming-of-age stories or memoirs about age-disparate love."

—D. Donovan, Senior Reviewer, Midwest Book Review

"*Half In* by Felice Cohen is both poignant and witty. Felice beautifully captures the angst she experienced growing into the person she was meant to become, helping us understand how our experiences, relationships, and connections shape us in ways we often don't realize until we are much older. *Half In* is a touching love story, coming-of-age story, coming out story, and growing up story that made me laugh and cry. I couldn't put it down and strongly recommend you pick it up. I'm all in with *Half In*."

—Lucy J. Madison, Author

"Beautifully written memoir that left me with a feeling of healing that can only come from recognizing the universality of life experience. I feel renewed in reading this book because I've realized that part of my own struggle is rooted deeply in past choices that I've not yet learned to accept and embrace."

—Suzie Carr, author of the critically acclaimed novel, The Dance

"I couldn't put this book down and read it straight through. The author's honest and provocative account of loving someone in secret and the futility of finding peace in the silence, will in retrospect, leave readers profoundly touched as the reminder of this memoir will play in your head like a cherished tune."

—Sally A. Monti, author of Light at the End of the Tunnel: A Memoir

Half In

A Coming-of-Age Memoir of Forbidden Love

Half In

A Coming-of-Age Memoir of Forbidden Love

Felice Cohen

~

Dividends Press

Publisher's Cataloging-In-Publication Data
(Prepared by The Donohue Group, Inc.)

Names: Cohen, Felice, author.
Title: Half in : a coming-of-age memoir of forbidden love / Felice Cohen.
Description: First edition. | New York, NY : Dividends Press, [2022]
Identifiers: ISBN 9798985701708 (paperback) | ISBN 9798985701715 (ebook)
Subjects: LCSH: Cohen, Felice. | Lesbians--Biography. | May-December romances. | First loves. | Self-acceptance. | LCGFT: Autobiographies.
Classification: LCC HQ75.4.C65 A3 2022 (print) | LCC HQ75.4.C65 (ebook) | DDC 306.76/63092--dc23

Cover design: Miladinka Milic www.milagraphicartist.com

www.felicecohen.com

Manufactured in the United States of America

Also by Felice Cohen

Books

What Papa Told Me

90 Lessons for Living Large in 90 Square Feet (...or More)

The Fancy Tale Series

Anthologies

I Bared My Chest

In the Shadows of Memory: The Holocaust and the Third Generation

Habits & Attitudes

The Future of Property

Grandmas & Grandkids

Personal Dedication

A Father's Advice

This book is my own personal experience and my memories of a certain period in my life. In some instances, events have been compressed, characters have been combined and dialogue has been re-created. The names and identifying characteristics of some persons described in the book have been changed for reasons of privacy. This is because this is not a book about the individuals I have described, but about my own experiences and how they shaped my life.

To Mom and Dad

For always loving, encouraging, supporting
and accepting me

Contents

Deja Vu: Watching Old Movies on the Late Night Show
By Rita Mae Brown

Once I saw you
When you were 27.
Strange to see you
At the point I find myself.
Film makes time and history optional,
Perhaps I'm 51
And you're 27?
No,
I am 27
And you are 51.
What does it matter, anyway?
You look much the same
Handsomer now—
Except
The years are rivers
Widening our conceits into slavery
Narrowing our arteries into cowardice.
Does age really bring with it knowledge
Or is it the knowledge of self-defeat?
Did you ever have a dream above applause?
Did you strike a hard bargain with the devil of fame?
And did you lose something along the way?
You did, I know you did.
Whisper then to me
Whisper the dream quickly
Lest I become older in this instant
Intoning a catechism of congratulation
For my mind that respects no boundaries.
Whisper it
So that I might grow rather than age.

Half In

A Coming-of-Age Memoir of Forbidden Love

Prologue
Friday, November 8, 2002

"Cancer craves sugar." Sarah's voice echoes in my head on this chilly November afternoon as I pull up behind four other cars already parked in front of her cottage in South Hadley, Massachusetts. I half expect Sarah to burst out the front door as she usually does upon my arrival, often wearing a colorful sweater, more recently her head hairless, shouting, "Where are they?" I am under strict orders to bring Krispy Kreme doughnuts at every visit.

But this time Sarah hasn't come out to greet me.

Walking up to the front door, I see Sarah's blue ten-speed bicycle—with two flat tires—leaning against a stack of firewood. Sarah had purchased that bike the previous year. At the same time, she had also purchased a new car, adopted two cats, and paid for my Lasik eye surgery, acts of celebration after the doctor had told her that her cancer was in remission. Two months later, we learned the doctor's diagnosis had been wrong.

Box of doughnuts in hand, I head inside.

Standing at the kitchen counter is Katherine, Sarah's girlfriend. Katherine introduces me to the hospice nurse beside her, saying, "Felice used to work for Sarah." Katherine doesn't know my real relationship to Sarah. No surprise. Few do.

Sarah's calico cat leaps onto the counter. "Hello, Louie!" I nose-kiss the cat, then put down the box of doughnuts. "Help yourself," I tell the women, "but save one for Sarah. They're her favorite."

"Felice." Rachel, my old friend, beckons me into the bedroom.

My breath catches. Sarah is lying in bed, her face sunken as though deflated, with deep shadows around her barely open eyes. Gone is Sarah's nightstand, along with the stack of books she was currently reading. In their place is a machine with multiple dials from which a clear plastic vacuum tube protrudes and ends inside Sarah's nostrils. With each of her laboring breaths, a mass of yellowish-brown mucus jumps and slides within the tube, making its way into the belly of the machine.

"Is she sleeping?"

"She slipped into another coma last night," says Rachel. "It would've been too late for you to come."

She woke from a coma just last week, I think. She could again.

The hospice nurse enters the bedroom and wraps her fingers around Sarah's bony wrist to check her pulse.

"Can she hear us?" I ask.

"We don't know." The nurse writes something on a clipboard. It's Sarah's clipboard, the same one she used at work before cancer forced her into retirement. "The hearing is the last to go, so talking to her couldn't hurt."

I stifle a laugh.

"Is that funny to you?" The nurse looks appalled.

"No. It's just what you said reminded me of this joke, where a woman brings chicken soup to a funeral and the funeral director says, 'It won't help.' And the woman replies, 'It couldn't hurt.'"

The nurse remains stoic, Jewish humor obviously not her thing. Uncomfortable, I look away and notice that the closet door is open. I step inside and switch on the light. On a high shelf, Sarah's sweaters are neatly folded and stacked by color, her pants and shirts hanging below in similar arrangements. Two weeks earlier, Sarah had insisted I switch her winter and summer wardrobes for the coming season, even though she and I both knew she wouldn't wear them again.

In the back of the closet, I expect to see Sarah's cat Sammy jump out, even though the cat had died years ago. Sarah had cried harder over Sammy's death than when her aunt had passed away at ninety-six.

I spot Sarah's briefcase tucked behind a plastic shelf unit. Inside is a book of poetry by Emily Dickinson, along with dozens of letters in my handwriting. I walk out of the closet with the briefcase.

"Sarah, Felice is here to see you," Katherine says. But the only sound from Sarah is the beat of her shallow breaths. Rachel and Katherine leave, closing the door behind them.

"Sarah, what are ya tryin' to do, make me sick?" I hope she might recognize the line by Roseanne Roseannadanna, our favorite Gilda Radner *Saturday Night Live* character, and give me her familiar smile. Instead of responding, Sarah's breathing grows more rapid. The gold cat charm resting in her neck's hollow rises and falls with each struggling breath.

I sit on my old side of the bed and remove the poetry collection from the briefcase. Several pages are bookmarked. I open to the first bookmark, a faded ticket stub from a James Taylor concert at Tanglewood, and skim the page. Not finding the poem that I'm searching for, I move to the second bookmark, a movie stub from *Schindler's List.* It, too, doesn't mark the right page. The third bookmark is a filmstrip from an arcade photo booth, the kind where you're expected to ham it up for the camera, which explains why Sarah and I are making goofy expressions in all four pictures. I glance at the page. There it is. I recite it softly to Sarah.

I died for beauty, but was scarce
Adjusted in the tomb,
When one who died for truth was lain
In an adjoining room.

He questioned softly why I failed?
"For beauty," I replied.
"And I for truth,—the two are one;
We brethren are," he said.

And so, as kinsmen met a night,
We talked between the rooms.
Until the moss had reached our lips,
And covered up our names.

Sarah's breathing grows louder. The ball of mucus in the tube jumps, and an orangey glow fills the room. The sun has begun its early descent.

Sarah's left arm rests on the blanket. I bring her limp hand to my chest, above my heart, and whisper, "Sarah, you're still there."

Without warning, Sarah takes a deep breath, as if gulping for air, and then exhales, her eyes opening wide. Her irises are as blue as I remember, though now milky. Is she waking up? Then her eyes shut and her breathing stops. I'm about to call out for the hospice nurse but stop myself when I glimpse the time on the cable box. It is just after four. "Our time," Sarah had called it, that last hour of the workday we used to spend together before going home to our separate lives.

Who the F--- Am I?
1991–1993

"This is nonsense!" The voice was irate but controlled. "If the president wants to give preference to outsiders over incoming students, tell him I'll be on the phone to the chancellor before he can blink an eye." Then came the sound of a phone slamming into its cradle.

Glad I'm not on the receiving end of that conversation, I thought as I stood on the third floor of the University of Massachusetts Amherst Undergraduate Admissions Office, trying to remember the receptionist's directions. Was the director of the New Students Program's office the last door on the left or the right? I took one more step and saw the woman who moments ago had been berating someone on the phone. Seated at a round table, facing the door, she wore a sky-blue shirt, collar up, and a navy sweater draped around her shoulders. She raked her fingers through her short hair—light brown with flecks of gray—and the strands returned in perfect array. It reminded me of a shampoo commercial that promised to make your hair manageable, something my long, unruly curls were not.

The woman peered at me over reading glasses perched on her aristocratic nose, her eyes as blue as her shirt. "Are you Felice?"

I nodded, my voice taking a leave of absence.

"What's wrong? Cat got your tongue?"

Heat rose to my cheeks as she stood, removing her reading

glasses, and letting them fall. They bounced against her chest, saved from the floor by the chain around her neck. As she stepped closer, she glanced at my feet, her eyes narrowing. Damn. I knew it had been a mistake to wear pink Top-Sider boat shoes to a job interview.

"Uh, no. Sorry, yes, I'm Felice." Yeah, I sounded as though I had the potential to help orient forty-five hundred new students.

"No need for apologies. At least not yet. I'm Sarah." She reached out her hand. Small, but the grasp firm. Our eyes were level. Surprising. From her forceful outburst on the phone, I'd assumed she'd be taller. She returned to her seat, and I sat across from her, catching my reflection in a poster-sized photograph of a cat on the wall, relieved my hair hadn't frizzed out from the humidity.

"Are you a cat person?" She must have assumed I was admiring the picture.

"I get that question often." I tugged on fake whiskers at the corners of my mouth. "I'm a human person, just haven't been to electrolysis in a while." Why had I said that? Because humor was my automatic reaction to nervousness. I wanted this job. For months my boss Rachel in Alumni Relations had been saying how invaluable working as a summer orientation counselor would be in my future career, no matter which path I took.

"Seriously, do you like cats?" Sarah asked. I was tempted to admit I'd hated them ever since a neighbor's tabby had once used my ten-year-old leg as a scratching post, but the other cat photos in the office told me that might impede my chances of landing this job.

"I had a golden retriever growing up," I said. Sarah half smiled.

I handed her my resume, and she put her glasses back on. As Sarah's eyes darted over my life's work, I scanned the room. The overhead fluorescent lights were off, and the two table lamps created a homey atmosphere. There was a desk in the corner with a computer on it; a bookcase filled with paperbacks of memoirs and poetry; and on top, a wooden sign with red letters that read NO WHINING.

Sarah looked up at me over the rims of her glasses. Her direct attention caused a warm tickle inside my stomach. "What would you say if a new student asks, 'Where's the best place to live on campus?'"

"I'd say go on a tour and don't decide based on advice from an older sibling who went here."

Sarah nodded. "What if a parent asks if there are parties in the dorms?"

"I'd say this is college. Of course, there are parties."

Her thin lips pursed. Tiny wrinkles creased around her mouth.

"But," I added, detecting my answer had been incorrect. "I'd tell them if they taught their kids good judgment, they should sleep fine at night."

Sarah offered a faint smile. Good save, Felice.

Resting her elbows on the table, Sarah clasped her hands as if in prayer. I noticed a silver double band on her ring finger. Was she married? "Every year I receive two hundred applications for twenty-four counselor spots. I hire those juniors and seniors with the best grades and who are active on campus. You'll lead tours and run meetings on adjusting to college life. You get a salary, plus room and board. What you won't get is much sleep, but you'll sleep enough when you're dead." Sarah said that last line in all seriousness. "I'll be honest with you. When Rachel gave me your name, I hoped you'd agree to an interview."

"You did?" Strange to hear she'd been talking about me. Nice, too.

"Both she and Coach Calipari gave you glowing recommendations. Also, I've read your columns in the *Collegian*. The one about your grandparents being Holocaust survivors was moving. Do you plan to pursue writing or work in your major?" She looked down at my resume. "Public relations and sports marketing."

"Pursue writing." Something about Sarah made me want to reveal the truth.

"Then do it," Sarah said as if that's all it took. "You've got great eye contact, you know that? That's my number-one qualification when hiring." She stared into my eyes. I tried to look away but couldn't. Her blue eyes had a hold on me. The tickle in my stomach kicked up seven notches. "Ms. Cohen, I'd like to offer you the job."

"Thank you." I stifled a grin, another auto response to nerves.

"Great." Sarah reached out her hand again. That time, I could have sworn her handshake lingered. "Talk to my secretary, Peg, about logistics. I'll see you in two weeks for training." Sarah picked up her phone and began dialing. When I didn't move, she looked at me as if wondering why I was still there. My time with her was over.

I bounded out of the building and raced down the walkway, exhilaration shooting through every limb. At North Pleasant Street I barely glanced at oncoming cars and buses before dashing across two lanes. Sprinting along the concrete corridor of the Fine Arts Center, I hurried down the wide steps to the edge of the Campus Pond. Students were scattered on the lawn studying for finals, sunbathing, or playing Frisbee. I turned up the hill toward Memorial Hall, a brick and sandstone two-story building inspired by the Italian Renaissance and constructed in honor of alumni and faculty who died in World War I, now home to Alumni Relations. At the entrance I paused, panting, and read the quote inscribed above the door: "We will keep faith with you who lie asleep." It made me think of Sarah's line of how you'll sleep enough when you're dead.

Sarah. She reminded me of past coaches, women who were tough and strong-minded. Determined to impress them, I'd worked hard, trying to gain their respect. Sarah would be no different, as her admiration seemed worth having. It didn't dawn on me that this could've been the outset of a crush. I opened the heavy door and hurried inside.

"I got the job!" I collapsed onto a rocking chair, the headrest imprinted with a large cursive U beside the block letters MASS, the same UMass logo on everything—sweatshirts, keychains, and water bottles—in Rachel's office. As associate director, Rachel handed out the swag at alumni events. My job, as her part-time office assistant, consisted of organizing it.

"I knew it." Rachel thumped her fist on her desk. Everyone assumed Rachel was my older sister. We each had shoulder-length curly brown hair, stood three inches above five feet, and had the same corny sense of humor. We'd met the summer before I'd arrived on campus at an event she was hosting for incoming freshman from Cape Cod. When Rachel had learned I was good at organizing, she'd offered me a job in her office. I'd been there ever since: three years and counting.

"Working for Sarah will change your life." Rachel folded back the sleeves of her button-down shirt. "She'll teach you leadership skills, how to run a program, and how to motivate people. Thanks to those two summers I worked for her, they hired me here right after graduation."

"Sarah's a little intimidating." I rocked back. "She makes me nervous, like I have to be on my best behavior."

"It's the power of her position. Everyone knows she doesn't put up with BS."

That jumpy sensation, like approaching the crest of a roller coaster, returned to my stomach. I planted my feet and stopped rocking. "Can I borrow your phone to call Parking? Peg said to wait until sessions started, but by then permits will be gone."

"If Peg said to wait, then that's coming from Sarah…"

"Come on, it's already May. Permits are probably gone anyway, so it won't even matter."

Rachel slid the phone across her desk. I picked up the receiver and dialed.

"Parking Services," answered a woman.

"Hi, I'm a counselor with the New Students Program." I exploited my minutes-old job title. "And I need a permit starting June first."

"What's your name?"

I gave my name and was put on hold. Plucking a UMass key chain from a basket on Rachel's desk, I slid it over my index finger. A few minutes later the line picked up.

"Seems you've been busy putting beans up people's noses. Didn't Peg say to wait before calling about parking?" Sarah was using the same sharp tone I'd heard from outside her office. How had she found out I'd called Parking? It was on the other side of campus. The same swirling in my stomach came on full force, this time for another reason.

"I only thought—"

"You thought wrong." Was she going to fire me before I even started?

"I'm sorry." I'd known her less than an hour and was already apologizing a second time. Not wanting to screw up again, I asked, "What do you mean about the beans?" Across from me, Rachel closed her eyes and shook her head slowly.

"It means don't do what you're told not to do," Sarah said, as though it were obvious. "When you tell kids not to put beans up their noses, what do they do?"

"Put the beans up their noses?" I guessed.

"Right. Now remember, better ten minutes early than one minute late. I'll see you at training." Sarah hung up.

"What happened?" Rachel slid her phone back.

"Someone at Parking forwarded my call to Sarah. Do you think she'll fire me?"

"No. Sarah may be hard-hitting, but she's fair. Everyone gets one chance to screw up." Rachel pointed a finger at the ceiling. "After that you're buh-bye."

Had I just used up my one? Then I had an idea.

"Thanks again for getting me the interview and for this." I lifted my hand, the key chain spun around my finger. "Maybe one day it'll hold the key to my future."

Outside, I ran past buildings, trees, residence halls, and students all the way to my car, which was parked on the outskirts of campus near the football stadium. Driving to the nearest supermarket, I moved quickly up and down aisles, grabbing a bag of legumes, a glass jar, and some ribbon, and then assembled them in my car before heading back to admissions. Standing outside Sarah's office, one hand behind my back, I waited for her to finish her call.

"Yes?" Sarah sounded annoyed when she looked over at me. Had coming back been a mistake?

"A peace offering." I walked in and handed her a glass jar full of kidney beans with a red bow on top. Sarah let out a hearty belly laugh. Few people, I came to learn, could make her do that.

Days later, still thinking about my parking-office blunder, I mailed Sarah a letter, hoping to smooth out any bad vibes before training.

May 18, 1991
Dear Ms. Hamilton,

I wanted to apologize again for the "beans up the nose" with the parking office. I didn't mean to cause a problem, but thought it was more convenient to park closer to the Northeast Residential Area where counselors live for the summer instead of having to schlep (in Yiddish this means to drag, haul, and get sweaty for no reason) my stuff from a far parking lot. I cannot wait to be an orientation counselor and hope you won't hold this bean against me.

Sincerely,

Felice

Sarah wasn't joking when she said sleep opportunities were sparse. Five days into orientation training, and I hadn't slept more than six hours a night. Every minute was spent absorbing details about academic requirements, facts about housing, and learning the route for leading campus tours.

I bonded quickly with fellow counselors over the lack of sleep and oppressive heat. Amherst, in Western Massachusetts, became a bowl of humidity in the summer. My alternative had been to go home to Cape Cod and work at a fish market again, but I wouldn't have traded this job for all the free lobster and ocean breezes in the world.

As excited as I was, Sarah still intimidated me. It didn't help that returning counselors, as we sat in the quad late at night sharing backrubs, shared stories of her past firings. Or that when Sarah explained the "beans up the nose" to the staff, she'd added, "If anyone needs an example, talk to Felice."

Wanting to impress Sarah, before our first session I went early to my assigned post outside Crabtree Residence Hall. My task was to chat with parents and direct new students where to sign in. I was standing, clipboard in hand, in the hot sun maybe three minutes, the only soul in the quad, when the front door of Crabtree sprung open, and Sarah came vaulting out. "What are you doing?" Her tone implied I was an idiot.

"Um, this is my post."

"And what time are you supposed to be at your post?"

"Five-thirty."

"What time is it now?" She rested her hands on her narrow hips, above a navy belt adorned with white golf balls.

I looked at my watch, the one item she required every counselor to wear. "Four forty-five. I'm early."

"Too early. Aren't there last-minute details you need to be doing?"

"No. Everything's done," I said. Sarah narrowed her stare. Did she not believe me? To help my case, I said I had things on my mind.

"Are you in love?" she asked.

What? Was this woman who was on a first-name basis with the chancellor really asking lowly me about my love life?

"No," I said.

"Well, whatever you're dealing with, suck it up." Then she marched back inside Crabtree, where she had her summer office, leaving me with the realization I'd killed any chance of being rehired the following summer.

Two months later, at the end-of-summer banquet in late July, Sarah rested a hand on my shoulder. "I hope you reapply next year. You were great."

I didn't stop smiling for days.

That September, I moved off campus into a two-bedroom apartment with a friend, also a senior. With *The Best of Van Morrison* blasting in my CD player, I disinfected the tiny, windowless bathroom while my roommate degreased the stove. In the middle of our Soft Scrub frenzy, the phone rang. Lauren, the *Massachusetts Daily Collegian's* new editor-in-chief, called to say I'd been selected to be a weekly columnist. I screamed with excitement.

"Another cockroach?" My roommate called out.

"We also want you to be the Jewish Affairs editor," Lauren said. The anti-Semitic incidents on campus the year before had convinced the school newspaper to institute the position. I was hesitant. Not because of my heavy course load, working two part-time office jobs, and giving campus tours on weekends, but because taking on that title meant putting myself out there as Jewish. I never hid my religion, but I never advertised it. My parents raised me Jewish, but I'd grown up on Cape Cod and identified more as preppy. The real issue was having my name in print as being Jewish. Yes, I'd written before about my grandparents being Holocaust survivors, and with a name like Cohen it was obvious, but having the title meant my name would be in the masthead, week after week, with the word "Jewish" beside it. My grandparents once had their names in print for being Jewish too. I wasn't fearful of the Holocaust happening again, but I was fearful of being targeted, the de facto reason they'd created the position.

Lauren was persistent. "Working as an editor is excellent practice for your writing, looks good on your resume, and comes with a desk in the newsroom."

That desk sealed the deal. That desk gave me credibility, allowed me to call myself a writer—which was odd, since writing had never been my thing. My thing had always been math. I'd arrived freshman year as a math major, and as a recruit for the women's Division I volleyball and softball teams. But college-level calculus—like college-level sports—was serious business and after a semester of unsolvable calculus equations and loathing playing the sports I'd loved since I was eight, I'd changed my major and quit both teams. With an abundance of free time on hand, I became treasurer of my dorm, got a second job as an office assistant in the men's basketball office, and became a DJ on WMUA, the college radio station.

One morning after hosting my radio show, I'd walked across the hall into the *Collegian* newsroom, approached a female student typing on a computer, and asked how someone gets to write for the paper.

"Easy," she'd said. "Come up with a story and write it."

Within a week I'd had my first article published, about students addicted to playing arcade games in the Campus Center. The op-ed editor had liked my style, and suggested I try writing opinion pieces. My first op-ed discussed the lack of female mascots in Division I colleges. One look at my byline had had me hooked, and I set my sights on becoming a weekly columnist. With many talented writers on staff, I'd first had to pay my dues.

The day I walked into the *Collegian* newsroom as a columnist and editor, I'm rather certain I strutted. Lauren, wearing an oversized maroon UMass sweatshirt, was directing reporters bent over keyboards trying to make deadline, and pointed to the back corner. "Felice, your desk's over there."

I walked to where the "special" editors' desks—Women's Affairs, Third World Affairs, Jewish Affairs, and Gay and Lesbian Affairs—sat packed together.

Two slender guys were sitting on the only desk not covered in newspapers, talking to a woman with a buzz cut seated at the adjacent desk. I said hi and told them they were sitting on my desk. Neither moved.

"You heard her," said the woman who had the deepest dimples I'd ever seen. "Move it."

The guys hopped off and sauntered out holding hands. I tried not to stare, but public displays of affection—gay or straight—made me uncomfortable.

"Sorry about that." The woman offered her hand. "I'm Heather, the Gay and Lesbian editor. I've known I was gay since I was ten."

"I'm Felice, the Jewish Affairs editor. I've known I was Jewish since birth."

Heather laughed so loud everyone looked over at us.

Over the next several weeks, I threw myself into my writing responsibilities. Opening the newspaper and seeing "Collegian Columnist" beside my name put me on cloud nine. The feedback kept me there. My columns were more personal than political. I wrote about waking at 5 a.m. to wait outside a professor's door to add a class, only to find I was tenth in line. Or about the surprise blind date my aunt had set up for me with the son of her friend when I'd arrived for a visit wearing sweatpants.

Each day I went early to the newsroom since in the afternoons I worked in the alumni and men's basketball offices. The only other person there was Heather.

One morning she trudged in, dropped her bag onto her desk, and sat on mine saying, "Had a crazy night at the North Star."

"What's the North Star?" I asked, pulling pages I'd been editing out from under her denim-clad thigh.

"It's a gay dance club in Northampton, and last night, both of the women I'm dating showed up. It's never been a problem since one goes to Smith and one goes here, but last night the dyke drama was crazy."

Why was she telling me this? Did she think I was gay? My image of gay women was based on popular stereotypes. And while a few fit my profile—I chose loafers over high heels and avoided lipstick—was that enough evidence to persuade a gay jury?

"Anyway." Heather slid off my desk. "Gotta go see my TA. Think she *like* likes me if you catch my drift."

"You are aware that Heather *like* likes you?" said a coarse voice after Heather had walked out. Startled to hear someone else in the newsroom, I swiveled around, which caused my chair to wobble. Tricia, the music editor, stood by her desk looking as one would expect a music editor to look: dark eyeliner, faded leather jacket, and a cigarette tucked behind one ear. Tricia didn't appear a reliable source for dating tips, but she had a talent for details. Had I missed something?

A week later, I was editing an op-ed about my first love, Edna (revealed at the end to be my first car, a blue 1980 Chevy Citation), when Heather walked in and sat in her usual spot—on my desk. She unwrapped a bagel and said she'd met a woman the night before at the North Star who reminded her of me.

"Why? Do I look gay?" I asked.

Heather assured me that being gay was not all about looks, but about personality, adding, "You'd have women lined up wanting to date you."

Tempting theory. Up to then, I'd dated a handful of boys, but that hardly constituted a line. I'd had my first "boyfriend" in sixth grade. He'd lived in Hyannis Port and was a first cousin to the Kennedys. It had lasted two months and had essentially consisted of sitting together on the school bus. In seventh grade there'd been my best friend's brother. During sleepovers, he would sneak into her room and we'd make out. This had continued until my friend got shipped off to boarding school in ninth grade.

At middle school parties we'd played spin the bottle and truth or dare. I'd always chosen dare. The thought of revealing my true feelings had scared me more than any dare a young teenager could've imagined. A fear that would follow me for life.

My freshman year of high school I'd had a crush on a senior girl in my public speaking class. She had straight chestnut hair she'd kept back with a headband, the color of which changed daily to match her Izod shirts. Her pale-green eyes looked made of glass. I'd gotten tongue-tied when she'd talked to me. (Though I'd had no problem speaking in front of the entire class, go figure.) But I'd never imagined kissing her.

During my senior year, I'd had a boyfriend, but had played it down, assuming "having a boyfriend" was synonymous with "having sex." And we weren't having sex. Not because I feared the act, but the stigma. The label "slut," so casually thrown around, hadn't been one I'd wanted sticking to me. To avoid being branded, I'd avoided outward displays of affection, even holding hands. And while we had fooled around in the family room after my parents had gone to sleep—he'd squeezed my breast while I'd stroked his exposed penis until something goopy had webbed through my fingers—I'd felt turned on but never satisfied. Teenage sex, I'd been convinced, existed merely for boys.

The summer after high school graduation, I'd worked at Chatham Fish and Lobster and had developed a crush on Josh. He was twenty-three, had a wide smile and long dark eyelashes. When summer had ended, I'd gone off to college, never expecting to see Josh again. A month later he'd shown up in Amherst, since he'd grown up in the area. We'd hung out, as neither of us had had many friends. Josh had gotten a job in town as a bartender at Judie's Restaurant, claiming he was trying to figure out the next stage of his life. I'd presumed someone twenty-three would've had his future planned out, but what had I known?

The first time Josh had kissed me—Halloween night, in his car outside my dorm, students walking by dressed as Freddie Krueger and the California Raisins—his tongue had run a full-court press inside my mouth. I'd welcomed the kiss but hadn't expected it, as I'd still been dating my high school boyfriend. After that kiss, the focus of my first semester was no longer about finding my way around campus but on finding my way around not going "all the way." Our fooling around had reached the point of his penis pressing against me, but I'd blocked it from entry thanks to my mom's voice in my head: "Losing one's virginity is something to save for when you get married. A special gift."

While home for Thanksgiving, I'd broken up with my high school boyfriend, then had raced back to Amherst and into Josh's waiting arms. But I'd never been in love with Josh or my high school boyfriend. I looked at Heather, sitting on my desk, chomping on a bagel. Had I been picking people from the wrong team?

"Aside from seeing someone in a gay bar," I said, "how can you tell if someone's gay?"

"We use gaydar. It's a vibe gay people get from other gay people." The levity in Heather's voice made it sound as though being queer wasn't a big deal. She said that some women didn't realize they were gay until college or even after marrying and having kids. "Sometimes all it takes is a kiss and then you know." She leaned close, lips puckered, eyes closed. My stomach twisted itself into a jumble of knots. I knew college was for experimenting, but the second I imagined kissing her, I panicked. If someone saw us, there'd be no unringing that bell.

Which is when Tricia entered the newsroom.

I hastily sat back. The sudden movement caused my chair to tip over, and I just missed cracking my skull against the Third World editor's desk. Kneeling by my side, Heather asked if I was okay.

"Yes," I said, then added, loud enough for Tricia to hear, "I'm sorry, but I'm not gay."

Heather helped me up, righted my chair and, without a word, walked out. The next day I found a note taped to my desk.

> Felice,
>
> Sorry about yesterday. I wish you were gay, but you say you're not, so I'll get over it. And don't worry, I changed my schedule, so I won't be around to make you uncomfortable.
> –Heather

On one hand, I felt relief, knowing Heather wouldn't try to kiss me again. On the other, disappointment. What if she'd been my one chance for a genuine relationship? This whole gay thing had me confounded. How did a person know if they were gay? I figured there must be books on the subject, so I went to Food for

Thought, the independent bookstore in Amherst, and skimmed every book on the gay and lesbian shelf, but none answered my question. Walking back to campus, I decided to ask someone.

"These questions are normal." Rachel stood behind her desk, which, along with the floor, was covered in plastic UMass water bottles. We were boxing them up to hand out at Homecoming. "I kissed a female counselor one summer, but it wasn't for me. What might be helpful is talking to a therapist."

"Therapy? You really think it could help?"

Rachel smiled. "Couldn't hurt."

"Call me Lynn." The therapist had short spiky hair (gay?) and wore brown Birkenstock sandals with thick wool socks. (Gay!) We spent a few minutes of getting-to-know-you chit chat. She asked where I was from, what my major was, and about my involvement on campus—easy questions, I realized, to get me comfortable before diving into the hard ones such as, "What brings you here?"

I stared at my loafers. "I want to know how someone knows if they're gay."

Lynn said there wasn't a simple answer, that some people know without a doubt, but for others, it takes longer. She asked if I thought I might be. My shoulders lifted and fell. The room felt stuffy. The tiny office inside the University Health Services had no windows, only a small desk, two upholstered chairs the color of mustard, and unflattering light.

"Does the thought of being gay scare you?"

I nodded.

"Why?"

"I want people to think I'm normal."

Her brow creased. Had I insulted her? I backtracked. "Not that I think there's anything wrong with being gay, but I wouldn't be comfortable standing out like that."

"But you write a weekly column read by thousands," she said. I explained the column, though personal, was about my opinion. She asked what had triggered my question and I told her about Heather liking me and my confusion as to how that made me feel.

"Have you thought of kissing Heather?"

"No." Sweat pooled in my armpits. "Maybe."

"How many men have you slept with?"
"Only one."
"And how was that experience?"

It had been the first night of Hanukkah my freshman year, less than a week after returning from Thanksgiving break. Josh had taken me to dinner to a fancy restaurant in Northampton and then to his apartment. His roommate was out of town.

"Be right back." Josh had left me in his bedroom and headed down the hall, saying over his shoulder, "Getting your gift."

After changing into a pair of his boxer shorts and one of his T-shirts, I'd sat on the mattress on the floor and braided my hair. Minutes later Josh had appeared wearing nothing except a red ribbon tied around his erect and very exposed penis. Hadn't he known the biggest present came on the eighth night of Hanukkah, not the first?

Josh had crossed the room. My eyes had been on his sizable dick, which, at my eye level, looked to be heading straight for my face. He'd lifted my T-shirt with one hand and tugged my boxers down with the other, signaling I should remove them myself. Then, like a magician who makes a coin appear from behind your ear, he'd been holding a small square foil package, which he'd ripped open with his teeth. After untying the ribbon, he'd flung it aside and rolled the condom down his erection. I'd watched, both fascinated and anxious. It had never occurred to me that I had a say in the matter.

Guiding me onto my back, he'd lowered himself on top. The dark hair on his chest tickled. In the last few weeks, we'd come close to having intercourse, as I'd put less faith in my wait-until-marriage vow, figuring it was only sex and not the end of the world. But when he'd inserted himself into me, it had felt damn close. I hadn't expected my skin to feel like it was tearing.

"Relax," he'd told me.

Yeah, right.

I remember holding my breath and staring up at him. His eyes had been squeezed shut as he'd raised and lowered his hips, his penis coming out before plunging deeper, reigniting the pain.

Thankfully, after a few minutes, Josh's body had tensed and, with a slight moan, he'd collapsed onto the mattress beside me, his penis slipping out. Sliding off the condom, he'd tossed it to the floor where it had landed near the red ribbon. Then he'd closed his eyes and fallen asleep. Excuse me, I'd thought at the time. Wasn't this supposed to be my Hanukkah present?

A month later, while I'd been home for winter break, Josh had broken up with me over the phone.

Lynn clipped her pen to her notepad. "Not the best first experience, which could explain why you're having thoughts about women. It could also be that Josh wasn't knowledgeable with how to please you, and you just haven't found the right guy. The dilemma you're having is more in your head than in your heart. We'll talk more next week."

But I didn't go back the next week. If the problem was in my head, then my head decided I wasn't gay, case closed. Besides, I had more pressing worries, namely the real world and all the unknowns that came with it—where would I live, what job would I have, and would I succeed—which would be arriving before I knew it.

On the last Saturday in October, I found myself standing in the same spot I'd stood the previous three Saturdays: inside the Campus Center Auditorium with half a dozen of my fellow summer orientation counselors, waiting to take the two-hundred visiting high school seniors and their parents on a tour of campus.

When the deans finished their spiels, Sarah, the emcee of those Saturday information sessions, closed the program by thanking everyone for coming. The crowd filed out to the lobby to gather materials on academics, housing, and financial aid. I was assigned thirty people and off we went. When the tour ended, I returned to box up leftover supplies.

"I was impressed with your column last week." Sarah, dressed in a navy suit with a crisp white shirt, approached me with a smile. My jeans and UMass sweatshirt, despite being the attire we were told to wear, made me feel underdressed. She leaned back on the table, hands resting on the edge, her demeanor lighter than normal. "I love how you compared your paternal grandmother,

Nana B., and her friends in Florida to those resourceful women stranded in the film *Strangers in Good Company*. Few young people are aware enough to admire those qualities."

"Thanks." I continued stacking campus maps inside a box.

"What did Nana B. think of it?"

"She loved it. Had me mail her a dozen copies to hand out to her friends. She's the self-proclaimed president of my fan club."

"You can sign me up for that club," Sarah said. "I look forward to reading your column every week."

"You do?"

"Absolutely." Sarah patted my arm, making me grin. I thought of my conversations with Heather and the therapist. Was this physical response confirmation of my gayness or was I simply reacting to Sarah's attention? Either way, I kept my head down until I was sure the flush in my cheeks had disappeared.

In late February, a month into the spring semester, I went to dinner with a friend at Woodbridges, a restaurant across the street from Mount Holyoke College where I was taking a sculpture class. In my four years at UMass, I'd taken advantage of the Five College Consortium, where students at any of the five colleges—UMass Amherst, Amherst College, Mount Holyoke College, Smith College, and Hampshire College—could take courses at the others for free.

While we were chatting over hearty soups, perfect for a cold winter night, someone approached our table. "Why, Ms. Cohen, what are you doing in South Hadley?"

At first, I didn't recognize Sarah. Like when I was in elementary school and had seen my teacher at the mall: this was totally out of context. Sarah apologized for interrupting my dinner, and said, "I just wanted to tell you I loved your column this week about how blonde jokes hurt everyone." She rested her hand on my shoulder (which sent a tingling sensation through my body), then walked away and sat at a table with three other women her age. When she placed a napkin over her lap, she looked back at me and winked.

"Someone from the Chancellor's office called," my roommate said. "Message is on the fridge." It was late April and I'd just returned from spring break, where I'd spent a week in Florida with Nana B.

The next morning, I called the Chancellor's office from the newsroom and learned I was one of two finalists to give the commencement speech.

"There's no way the 'feel-good' writer won't get picked," Lauren said, referring to the letter a reader had written to the *Collegian* saying my columns made her feel good.

That afternoon I found myself standing at one end of a long table inside the chancellor's conference room across from two women and two men, all in suits. The view outside was of the Haigis Mall, and I told the committee how my freshman year, I had spent hours looking for Haigis Mall, thinking it was a shopping center and not a promenade. After getting a laugh, I read my speech.

"Thank you," said one of the women. "We'll be in touch."

Filled with adrenaline, I hurried down the hall and almost bumped into someone approaching from around a corner.

"We have to stop meeting like this." Sarah was grinning, despite the fact I'd almost knocked her down. "What are you doing in Whitmore?"

"I just auditioned to give the commencement speech."

Sarah gave my bicep a gentle squeeze. "I'm sure you'll get it."

I walked away smiling so hard my cheeks hurt, a reaction from either the feel of Sarah's fingers lingering on my arm or from imagining myself addressing over four-thousand fellow graduates.

By the time I got back to my apartment, there was a message from the Chancellor's office.

"You were great," said the woman from the committee when I called her back. "We know you'll make UMass proud in the future, but I'm sorry to say you weren't picked."

I hung up the phone, crawled into bed, and cried.

Graduation came and went. I moved back into the dorms, as Sarah had rehired me to work summer orientation. I once again bonded with fellow counselors, particularly a first-time counselor named Kimberly who still had two more years of school. She had four older brothers, was the first in her family to attend college, and had a Boston accent so heavy I accused her kindergarten teacher of skipping the letter R. We spent our free time assembling jigsaw puzzles while singing along to Janet Jackson. But it was after seeing *A League of Their Own*, the two of us bawling through the closing credits as Madonna sang "This Used to Be My Playground," that we became inseparable.

When orientation sessions ended in late July, a professor hired Kimberly to house sit in August, and she asked me to help. With no other plans, I stayed. We spent our days hiking Mount Sugarloaf, gazing out at green trees, red barns, and white church steeples that dotted the landscape of the Connecticut River Valley. At night we played pool at a honky-tonk bar in Sunderland, ignoring the cat calls from men whose fingernails were permanently stained from working at nearby farms and auto-repair shops.

One morning I drove to Bruegger's Bagels in Amherst to pick up breakfast and bumped into an orientation counselor from my first summer. Dawn was holding a large coffee cup, her lipstick staining the lid. "Have a job?" she asked. Already I hated that question. She told me admissions was looking to hire a green dean for September, explaining it was a fancy title for an assistant director given to one UMass graduate each year. The job entailed traveling in the fall to high schools in New York and talking about UMass. In the winter you worked in the office and read college applications, and in the spring organized a reception on campus for incoming students.

"After working for Sarah," Dawn said, "you'd be a shoo-in."

Warm bagels in hand, I drove to admissions and filled out the application in the lobby. Landing that job meant putting off the real world for one more year. I'd never wanted anything more.

August 26, 1992

Dear Sarah,

Thank you for writing a recommendation letter for me to be the green dean. During my interview the admissions director said it was you telling her she'd be "crazy" not to hire me that cemented their decision. Green dean seems

> the next logical step after orientation counselor, a job I loved. Rachel said working for you would be life changing. She was right. I learned so much. And I'm not just talking beans up the nose.
>
> Thanks again.
>
> Felice

I spent my first fall as a college graduate visiting almost fifty high schools and answering the same questions: "What are the academic requirements?" "What do I need on the SATs?" "How big are the dorm rooms?" I loved the job but missed my new apartment. The ten-by-fifteen-foot studio, located inside a renovated pocketbook factory in Amherst, had been love at first sight when Dad had driven me up in late August to look at places. It had one wall of floor-to-ceiling hanging bars and storage cubbies that appealed to my organizing soul. At the opposite end was the kitchen, if you could call it that. It consisted of a mini fridge, two-burner stove, tiny sink, and two cabinets. A sizable window overlooking the parking lot filled the tiny space with late-day sunlight. The apartment also shared a bathroom with a female graduate student in an identical studio.

The job had me out of town for weeks at a time, so I gave Kimberly a key to collect my mail and for her to have a quiet place to get away from her dorm, where she was a resident assistant. I loved coming home to discover notes and candy she'd left for me. It had been a long time since I'd had a best friend.

One Friday night in early October, I returned to find Kimberly standing at my stove, the smell of oregano and tomatoes in the air.

"Welcome home." Kimberly piled spaghetti and sauce onto two plates.

"Happy to be home, even if it's only for two days." I left my suitcase by the door and collapsed onto the futon. "Whatever you're making smells delicious."

"My mom's recipe, and I made it for you." Kimberly sat beside me and gave my thigh a lingering squeeze. I froze. The questions concerning my sexuality, the ones I'd put into the recesses of my mind the year before, came whooshing back. Was she making a move? Did she like me? Should I say something? What if I did and it was a misunderstanding? I didn't want to lose her as a friend. At that point, all my friends had scattered to the wind. So I said nothing, but the spigot of thoughts had reopened, and as hard as I tried, shutting them off was impossible.

Two nights later I arrived at my Uncle Mark's apartment in the Bronx. I had a school visit nearby the next morning. Wearing sweatpants and a Yankees T-shirt, he greeted me at the door, bending his six-foot frame down to hug me. "Perfect timing. Dinner just arrived."

I cut through his galley kitchen into a small dining area. A faux Tiffany lamp hung above a round table covered with Chinese-food containers. Outside, the sun was setting over the treetops of Van Cortlandt Park.

With half of his attention on the New York Jets game on the TV, he listened to me talk about my job. I had begun writing *Notes From the Road*, funny anecdotes about highway mishaps (like the time my car had died in the middle of the Mass Pike at night) or hotel incidents (such as when another guest had been given my same room key and walked in on me getting dressed.)

"Speaking of writing." Mark picked up a sparerib. "Papa wants you to call him. Says he has another story for the book. I thought you were writing his Holocaust experience for the family. Now it's going to be a book?"

"I doubt it will be a book. That's just how Papa speaks."

A year earlier, after my grandfather had read my column in the *Collegian* about my grandmother, Fela, his first wife, surviving Auschwitz only to later take her own life, he asked me to write his story. He had never spoken with anyone, including his three kids, about his experiences in the camps. I assumed he would tell it to me from beginning to end, but my grandfather's memory didn't work that way. He'd remember a little from this labor camp, then a little from that concentration camp, then a story from before the war. Thank goodness I was good at puzzles. Dad thought Papa was able to speak freely to me because he felt less responsibility burdening a grandchild, adding that it was good for Papa to unload his secrets.

Speaking of secrets.

I'd woken up that morning dying to say something to Kimberly, who'd been lying beside me. She'd slept over many times, but after she'd touched my leg two nights earlier, I'd felt an underlying current running between us. I'd wanted to share my feelings, but what if I had misinterpreted her gesture? Plus, I wasn't sure if I *like* liked her. Perhaps I was just lonely since my social life had evaporated after graduation. I figured I'd ask Mark as I'd always been able to talk to him without fear of judgment. We were eleven years apart, closer in age than he was to my mom, making him more an older brother than an uncle. When I was in college, I'd visit him often. We'd spend weekends playing Backgammon, going to the theater, and eating at restaurants all over Manhattan.

I rested my chopsticks across my plate. "Did you know today is National Coming Out Day?"

Mark looked at me over his gnawed sparerib, his chocolate-brown eyes sizing me up. Wiping his sticky fingers on a napkin, he said, "Since you're asking, I assume you know."

"Know what?" I was suddenly confused.

"That I'm gay."

"You are?"

"Isn't that why you brought it up?" He pushed his glasses higher on his nose, leaving a mosaic of greasy fingerprints on the lenses.

"No. Why would I think that? You had a girlfriend in college. She came to my bat mitzvah."

"I was trying to be straight." He lifted a piece of broccoli to his mouth. "But if you didn't know about me, why'd you bring it up?"

"Because I think I may be."

"What makes you think that?"

"I have feelings for my friend Kimberly, but I don't have gaydar so I'm not sure she's gay."

Specks of broccoli flew from his mouth onto his plate as he laughed. He assured me gaydar was not a reliable barometer and I shouldn't worry about labeling myself. Then he asked if I'd thought about having sex with Kimberly. I admitted I didn't understand how two women had sex and he explained that they go down on each other.

"Gross." I crumpled my nose. "Maybe that means I'm not gay."

He laughed. "You're preaching to the choir. Have you ever gone down on a man?"

That sounded worse. He reassured me that when I was in love with someone, man or woman, I'd feel differently. I wasn't physically attracted to Kimberly as I had been to Josh, but something inside me lit up when I saw her. Maybe I did have feelings for her or maybe it was curiosity. Either way, Mark said I didn't need to figure it out that minute. So, I didn't.

A few months later in mid-January, Kimberly and I were lying on my futon, facing each other in the dark, her warm breath on my skin. A sharp wind hissed against the window. The only light came from an outdoor floodlight and the occasional headlights crawling up the wall when a car pulled into the lot.

My brain had been pushing me to tell Kimberly how I felt about her since I'd picked her up two hours earlier in front of her dorm, but my fear kept me silent. What if she freaked out? I'd almost said something after my talk with Mark last October, but Kimberly had started dating a guy in her poetry class. During winter break, they'd broken up and I swore to myself I'd say something when she returned to school because holding this feeling inside was eating me up. I reasoned that if she didn't reciprocate, then I could at least move on.

"I feel I've known you my entire life and can tell you anything," I said.

"You can."

"I've had many best friends, but with you something is different." I grabbed at the words spinning around my head like objects caught in a tornado. "I like you as more than a friend."

Kimberly didn't respond. The silence was deafening. Was she mad? Had I ruined everything?

"I'm sorry," I said. "I didn't mean to upset you. I understand if you don't feel the same. I'm not even sure what I'm feeling."

Kimberly rested her hand on my arm. "Every time I slept with the poet, I thought of you."

Elation. Delight. Joy. Then fear. Now what? Luckily Kimberly knew. She pressed her plump lips against mine. Her tongue didn't pry its way into my mouth as most guys I'd kissed had done. Instead, it was gentle, tasteful. I eased into it, then grew nervous.

Which one of us was supposed to initiate the next move? And what exactly was the next move? At least with men, sex seemed straightforward (no pun intended): A went into B. But we had two Bs. And as great as I was at puzzles, I found myself stumped.

Kimberly removed her T-shirt, took my hand, and brought it to her firm breast, which fit perfectly in my palm. She prodded me to squeeze. Her nipple hardened between my fingers. "That feels good." Her talking added to my unease. Conversing during sex had never been my thing. Though until that point, neither had sex. Kimberly had been having sex with guys since she was sixteen. It didn't bother me she had more experience, but it amazed me how comfortable she was telling me what turned her on. I hadn't a clue what turned me on. Maybe because up until then, no one had ever asked.

Kimberly coaxed my other hand south, slipping it inside her underwear, guiding my fingers along a ridged, damp spot. Nervousness turned to terror.

"Yes! Touch me there!" she cried. I debated asking her to keep her voice down for fear of disturbing my neighbor. As though reading my mind, Kimberly dragged a pillow over her face. "Go inside," she said, the pillow muffling her voice.

What!

When I didn't budge, Kimberly took hold of my middle finger and guided it. Soft, fleshy walls enveloped my entire digit. She moved me in and out before letting go, leaving me to run the show.

My arm soon cramped. I debated switching to my other hand when her insides tightened and loosened in pulsing waves, followed by a rush of warm wetness. A muffled squeal escaped from beneath the pillow, which Kimberly slid to one side. Damp strands of hair stuck to her face. She rolled into me, her cheek against my chest. I draped my arm around her as the wind slipped in through tiny gaps in the window.

"Are you okay?" Even though I owned the same equipment, chances were good I might've screwed something up. I assumed she'd had an orgasm but couldn't be sure. No one had ever made my body respond that way.

"More than okay. Now I want to please you." Kimberly sat up, tied her long hair into a ponytail, and planted her hands on my breasts, moving in a similar pattern to my earlier moves. Was that gay sex? Was everything even-steven? Would she expect me to guide her hand? "Tell me what you like," she said, confirming my fear.

I liked Mel Brooks movies and red licorice.

"What you're doing is fine," I said.

"Don't you ever touch yourself?" she asked. How could I tell her that each time I'd tried, doing so had left me feeling as though I were about to take a final exam after having missed every class: unprepared and clueless.

Kimberly moved her hand in the same way she'd guided mine. It caused a minor sensation, but nowhere near close to what she'd experienced. Not wanting to hurt her feelings, I mimicked her same moans, which satisfied Kimberly, if not me. I chalked it up to this being my first time with a woman, and perhaps I was too self-conscious. Next time would be better.

As we lay spooned, I stared out the window, my brain running wind sprints. I'd now had sex with a man and a woman, and neither had left me satisfied. Was something wrong with me?

Within a month, Kimberly had used the L-word, but how could she be in love so soon? I liked her—but love? How did one even recognize that emotion? Being in love seemed arbitrary and indefinite. Kimberly loved with all her heart even if it meant getting hurt. That vulnerability frightened me. It's probably the reason I couldn't have an orgasm. Letting go meant putting my trust into someone else's hands. Literally.

We continued to sleep together, and I continued not to have orgasms while Kimberly sometimes had two or three in a row. I was too much in my head, worrying about what she was thinking or if I was doing it right. I cared for Kimberly but wondered if not enjoying the sex verified that I wasn't gay. Then again, the sex I'd had with Josh was worse, so where did that leave me? Did you need to be in love with someone to enjoy sex?

Kimberly knew she was gay, had no problem with it, said she was done with men, even though I was the first woman she'd been with. It amazed me how sure she was in her declaration. I envied her contentment as I feared choosing a category. Why come out of the closet when I couldn't be sure my only reason for being in there wasn't just to organize it? Since I wasn't ready to claim full membership, I made Kimberly promise to keep us a secret. I knew it pained her, hiding what was inside her heart, but she went along with it thinking I would soon come around.

"Want to grab lunch?" Sarah stood in my office doorway, baby-blue sweater highlighting her blue eyes. Her short hair, as usual, perfect. I readjusted my ponytail. Would I ever sport a grown-up hairdo?

"Sure." What else was I going to say?

"Great. Meet me at my car in a half hour. It's the silver Mazda."

It was April and I had spent the last few months chained to my desk, reading applications and planning an event for incoming freshmen. The handful of times I'd seen Sarah around the office building, she had always greeted me with a smile, asked how the job was going, and if I'd been doing any writing. Heat would rise to my cheeks. I knew it was a crush, but now that I was dating Kimberly and had entered the lesbian world, the crush felt dangerous in the sense of its possibility. Not that Sarah would ever be interested in me, I felt, but still.

I called Rachel the second Sarah walked out. "Why do you think Sarah's asking me to lunch?"

"Could be she's hungry." Rachel was no help.

"What are your plans after the green dean job ends in June?" Sarah asked. We were inside Panda East, the popular Chinese restaurant in downtown Amherst, seated beside a large fish tank filled with yellow fish. It was quiet as the lunch crowd had yet to arrive.

"Nothing yet. It's a question I try to avoid."

"Could I interest you in being the night director this summer?"

"Isn't the night director an experienced residence director? I was never even an RA." Sometimes I just opened my mouth and stuck my foot right inside. Here she was offering me a job, which meant putting off the real world a little longer, and there I was pointing out my lack of qualifications.

"Doesn't matter. I know you can do it." What Sarah didn't know was that Kimberly and I were a couple. And since Sarah had already rehired Kimberly as a head counselor and was against coworkers dating, I doubted she'd have been offering me the job as her assistant if she knew. But Kimberly and I had been keeping our relationship under wraps for three months. What were another three? Sarah plucked a fried noodle from a bowl. "So, what do you say?"

"I say I promise not to put beans up anyone's nose."

She laughed. "I'll hold you to it."

The warm May air blew our long hair all over the place as Kimberly and I cruised along moonlit back roads. She had been asking me for weeks to go to the North Star, but I feared seeing someone I knew, or, rather, them seeing me as I was still on the fence about my sexuality. When Kimberly heard about Our Hideaway, a lesbian bar in Chicopee, a half hour from Amherst, I gave in.

Turning onto a dirt road riddled with potholes, we passed dogs barking from behind a chain-link fence guarding a discount-tire store. Next to it was a rundown building bathed in a sinister hue from dim streetlights. Our Hideaway.

The entrance was plastered with pictures of colorful and various-shaped dildos for sale. I elbowed Kimberly.

"Want to get one?" she asked.

God no.

There were also fliers: "Join our softball team." "Sign up for our pool league." "Come to our LOO Bed and Breakfast in Provincetown."

"I wonder what LOO means," I said.

"Lesbian owned and operated."

"How do you know that?" I asked. But Kimberly didn't hear; she was halfway to the bar, shoulders back, head high, as though she were a regular. It amazed me how comfortable she appeared. I avoided eye contact with anyone and quickened my pace to catch up.

The women, mostly in their thirties and forties, wore flannel shirts with shorn haircuts. Their eyes turned to us: fresh meat. Or so I felt. The bartender, sporting a white men's undershirt beneath a men's leather vest, poured amber liquid over a row of shot glasses.

"She looks tough," I whispered to Kimberly.

"You know what they say, 'Butch in the streets, femme in the sheets.'"

No, I didn't know they said that.

Kimberly walked over to a small chalkboard near the pool table and added her name. I spied two women making out on the dance floor to Whitney Houston's "I Will Always Love You" and shivered. How were they not embarrassed to show affection in public?

Soon it was our turn at the pool table. The stockier of our opponents broke, sending rainbow-colored balls across the table. None dropped. I sank one, the taller opponent sank two, and then Kimberly cleared the table. Our competitors raised their unkempt eyebrows. Kimberly's brothers had begun teaching her to play when she was five.

We won that game and the next two, drawing high fives from strangers. Feeling as though I were being viewed as an athlete rather than a lesbian, I walked confidently to the bar to replenish our drinks.

"You've got beautiful eyes," said a woman with a raspy voice, leaning close and revealing ample cleavage. "I've never seen you here. Is this your first time?"

Before I answered, a cue stick appeared between us. "Your turn," Kimberly said. As I walked away, I heard Kimberly tell the woman to go find her own girlfriend. Unease spread through me. Girlfriend implied I was a full-fledged lesbian, a word I was still uncomfortable saying, let alone identifying with.

Training week that summer flew, as my to-do list filled up faster than I could cross items off. Sarah was right, though. No one cared about my resume, only that whatever needed to get done got done. And she had trained me to get stuff done. My responsibilities included maintenance issues in the dorms, disciplining anyone caught with alcohol, and addressing hundreds of new students on choosing their housing each session from the stage in Mahar Auditorium, where I'd taken lecture classes as an undergraduate. Sarah also left me in charge when she went home each night. But the most daunting part of the job was sharing an office with her.

On the first day, as we set up our desks, Sarah explained that Crabtree Hall got its name from Charlotte "Lotta" Crabtree, the highest-paid vaudevillian performer in the 1800s, who had given scholarships to UMass students. Sarah loved history as much as aphorisms—her favorite being the one she uttered every year on the first day of training: "When you make pancakes, the first one often gets burnt, like the first session. After that, each pancake comes out better."

And that first session? Beyond scorched. Luckily, Sarah ran her program the same every summer: same procedures, same routines, same checklists. And those guidelines enabled us to navigate whatever obstacles appeared. Such as when the dining hall had to close for a week of renovation and we were forced to find an alternative to feed hundreds of new students three meals a day. Or when the university rented acres of athletic fields to a caravan club of airstreams, and we had to reroute our parent bus tours. It was challenging, but I loved every minute of it.

Sarah put a lot of faith into me, and I wanted to do a good job. Which was why when Kimberly stopped by early one morning and shut the office door, wanting one kiss, I said no.

"Come on, live a little," she pressed.

We hadn't spent a night together since training had begun over a week before. Honestly, I was glad. I'd grown weary of the sex. I was content to please her but was tired of faking it on my end. Figuring I owed her one kiss, I gave in. Wouldn't you know the second our lips met, the door handle turned, and my heart almost shot out of my chest.

"These all came in this morning, sugar." Sarah's secretary, Peg, handed me several pink phone messages, which no doubt matched the color of my cheeks. Did she know what we'd been doing?

Peg, in her mid-fifties, was a former beauty pageant winner from Mississippi who, a decade earlier, had moved to Western Massachusetts with her third husband. After they'd arrived, he'd left her for a younger woman. "Just as well," Peg had said. "He was horrible in the sack." Peg could often be mistaken for a truck driver in drag the way the hearty insults flew from her lipstick-stained mouth. She'd once given me a ride home, and when someone had honked, she'd yelled out the window, "The horn blows! Does the driver?" Even if Peg knew what we'd been doing, she'd probably done worse. Regardless, after that incident I swore I'd never compromise my work again.

Minutes later Sarah walked in and placed her briefcase onto her desk, asking the same question she asked every morning: "Any surprises last night?"

Before I responded, a female counselor ran in shouting that she had bugs in her room. Natalie was a drama major, which meant everything in her life was a drama. Sarah called her a first timer, which in Sarah-speak meant clueless. I told Natalie I would have maintenance spray her room. She left and as I added the task to my to-do list, my phone rang.

"Hi. This is Ron from Valley Vending returning your call."

"Hi, Ron," I said. "Our vending drink machines are empty. We have parents arriving tomorrow and because of the heat need them refilled today."

"No can do. It'll have to be next week." If I relayed his message to Sarah, she'd tell me to find another way.

"Well, if you can't come today, when you come next week, you can remove the machines. I'm sure another company would appreciate the college's business," I said. Sarah turned her head in my direction.

"Fine," said Ron. "We'll have someone this afternoon."

"Overwhelmed yet?" Sarah asked when I hung up.

"No. I look at it like a jigsaw puzzle. Many pieces to fit together."

"I don't have patience for puzzles, but I do for these." Sarah stepped over and handed me Xeroxed pages from a book. "One of my summer traditions is having the night director memorize poems. It's my way of sharing my love of poetry."

"Memorize poetry? I don't remember that in my job description." I skimmed the two poems. One was by Emily Dickinson and another by a woman named Rita Mae Brown.

"It falls under 'other duties as assigned.'"

"You mean there could be more?"

Ever since we'd begun sharing an office, the edges of Sarah's tough exterior had softened and an easygoing lightness had appeared. I assumed it was because I was now a boss and privy to another side of her. In return, I became more relaxed, which is why I replied to this task by saying, "Bite me."

Sarah's eyes opened wide. Okay, maybe too relaxed.

"Sarah, can I talk with you?" Tim, a first-year counselor, was standing at the door, clipboard in hand, his long legs sticking out of plaid Bermuda shorts. Tim was student government president and had used his "one" during training when he'd overslept and missed the session on how to proctor placement exams.

"What is it?" Sarah's tone had none of the buoyancy it had had moments ago.

"I can't lead the campus tour tomorrow morning."

"Why not?" Sarah despised the word "can't." Whatever excuse he uttered had better include a dead relative.

"I have no clean clothes." At least he was original.

"Nothing?" Sarah asked.

"Just my bathrobe."

"What do you think, Felice?" Sarah leaned back on my desk and folded her arms.

"Why not wear that and call it the Bathrobe Tour?" I joked.

"Brilliant idea. From now on, that's what we'll call the morning tour. I bet it will even attract more students. What do you know, Tim? Problem solved." Sarah turned her back on him, making it obvious the conversation had ended. Tim loped away.

"Amazing what comes out of that curly head of yours." Sarah tapped my head, sending butterflies racing down my neck.

Footsteps smacked noisily in the hallway and a female counselor ran into our office. "A student left her curling iron on in her room and locked herself out!"

Calmly, I opened my desk drawer, pulled out a metal ring the size of a dinner plate, the sole master key dangling from it, and asked, "How long has the iron been on?"

Sarah and I ate lunch together every day that summer. I found myself looking forward to when she would stand up, remove her glasses, place them on her desk, and say, "Let's go." I'd stop whatever I was doing, and we'd walk to the Franklin Dining Commons, about a half mile away. Usually this walk took me less than ten minutes, but when walking with Sarah I'd have to slow my pace. I didn't mind though. I loved those carefree strolls under the summer sun talking about books, movies, even our childhoods. Sarah had grown up in Pennsylvania with her mother and older brother, her father having died when she was young. I didn't remember from previous summers if Sarah ate lunch with the night director daily, but she was big on routines, so it was probable.

One day, seated at "our table" near a wall of enormous windows overlooking campus, the twenty-eight-story tower library in the distance, Sarah asked, "Did you memorize the poems?"

I nodded as I swallowed my bite of tuna-fish sandwich.

"Great. Let's hear the Emily one." Sarah sounded playful but adamant. She was as serious about poetry as she was about cats. Ever since her assignment two weeks before, I'd wondered if the poems were the same every summer or if she selected them specifically for each night director. And if so, had she given me the Rita Mae Brown poem—"She came at that precise junction in a life / when the past is unbearable / and the future uncertain"—because she was trying to tell me something? Or was it just my budding crush creating far-fetched scenarios?

"I died for beauty. . ." As I recited the Emily Dickinson poem, I caught Kimberly's eye a few tables away. She was sitting with two counselors, breaking Sarah's no-clumping rule. Only two counselors could sit together, since their job was to talk to new students, not one another. And my job was to make sure the counselors did theirs.

"Excellent." Sarah reached across her tray and placed her hand on mine just as Kimberly approached.

"There's a student's cah with a flat pahked behind Crabtree." Kimberly's gaze was on Sarah's hand resting on mine.

"What's the license plate?" I slid my hand out from beneath Sarah's and reached for my clipboard. What must Kimberly have been thinking? What would anyone think? After Kimberly walked away, Sarah put two pink pills into her mouth.

"Flintstones?" I joked.

"Estrogen replacement." Sarah picked up her water glass. "Which is something else you can learn from me. Don't get old." I didn't tell her I planned to be twenty-three forever. "Tell me."

Sarah washed down the pills. "As an athlete, does your repertoire of sports include golf?"

"Don't they say golf gets in the way of a good walk?"

"Tell you what, smartass, let's play tomorrow. If you win, I'll buy you lunch. And if I win, lunch is on you."

"Okay," I said. Saturday was our only day off and I usually spent it with Kimberly. She would be livid.

That night I woke from a dream in which Sarah showed up at my apartment, told me her girlfriend had left her, and kissed me. I tried falling back to sleep, but my brain was hellbent on replaying the dream. I grabbed my journal from the nightstand and wrote under the glow of the building's outdoor floodlight.

I'd been journaling since middle school. We had just read *Night* by Elie Wiesel and my mother had come into the class to speak about her parents' experiences in the Holocaust. Uncomfortable with the emotions that had bubbled up in me, I'd walked out. After that, my English teacher had suggested journaling as a safe space to vent my feelings. Since that time, I had filled dozens of journals, chronicling the usual teen angst—liking boys who didn't like you back, body-image concerns, fights with friends. The journaling had continued throughout college, and even after, writing about my questions regarding my sexuality and my apprehensions about entering adulthood.

But that summer, the entries focused on Sarah—mainly our conversations and the exhilaration I felt whenever I was around her. I knew it was risky to write them down, but when I found myself obsessing, I had no choice. Writing stopped these thoughts from preoccupying my mind and helped me make sense of them.

"What are you doing?" Kimberly snuggled up behind me. "It's the middle of the night."

"Crazy dream. Couldn't sleep."

"Why don't you dream of the French toast we'll eat at Sylvester's?"

I glanced back over my shoulder. "Save me a piece."

"You're not going? The entire staff is going to brunch."

"I'm playing golf with Sarah, remember?"

"But Saturday's our day." Kimberly's tone reminded me of

Sarah's no-whining rule. No wonder Sarah had had the sign made. Everyone needed a reminder.

"Come on, it's part of the job."

"Yeah, yeah, other duties as assigned," Kimberly said in a mocking tone. "Do you like Sarah?"

Do I what! Had Kimberly read my journal? Instinctively I closed it. "Why would you ask me that?"

"Because we haven't had sex in forever." She traced her hand down my hip.

"We've been tired."

"I haven't been *that* tired. Is something wrong?"

Could I tell her something had felt wrong since the beginning, but I'd stuck it out because the closeness we shared made me think the sex part just needed time to catch up?

No, I could not.

"Nothing's wrong," I assured her. "Please don't be upset I'm playing golf with Sarah."

"All the returning counselors agree Sarah's more laid-back this summer because of you. I bet she likes you. It gives me the creeps just thinking about a woman in her fifties liking someone almost a third her age." Hearing Kimberly verbalize my exact worry justified my reasons for keeping my thoughts to myself.

Early the next morning, the sun strong, the air smelling of fresh cut grass, I stood at the first hole of the Cherry Hill Golf Course in Amherst, taking practice swings with Sarah's driver. My confidence was, for the first time, that of a kid always picked last in gym class. I'd been a three-sport varsity athlete in high school and recruited to play on two Division I college teams, but with Sarah's full attention on me, I wanted to impress.

"Keep your eye on the ball, bend your knees, breathe." Sarah's short hair had mushroomed over the top of her white visor. I did as she instructed and my ball sailed down the fairway, landing a few yards farther than hers. Sarah eyed me suspiciously. "I thought you'd never played."

"I played putt-putt growing up. Didn't think it counted."

At the second hole, as I lined up my shot, Sarah wrapped her arms around me from behind to correct my grip, her chest pressing against my back. A fluttering filled my stomach.

"Do I have to pay extra for that?" I joked. Sarah released her hold and stepped back. Was she upset? Didn't she know I was joking? Rattled, I sent the ball zipping along the fairway like a stone skipping across a lake.

"Worm burner," Sarah said as we got into the cart, which she let me drive. My thighs stuck instantly to the plastic cushion. Only 8 a.m. and already humid.

"What is it about golf you love so much?" I asked, hoping to detract attention from my comment.

"Just look around." Sarah tilted her chin forward. "The apple trees, the view of the Berkshire Hills. This is God's country."

"Want to guess my favorite part?" I pressed down on the gas pedal and spun the wheel to the left, making a doughnut on the green.

"Stop!" Sarah grabbed the front bar. I pulled over, and she touched my cheek, saying, "That devilish grin," which caused the contents of my stomach to perform circus-sized backflips. "Tell me, was Kimberly okay with you playing golf with me?"

What? I tried to keep my expression blank, but I had no poker face.

"You should've told me you were dating. That's a huge surprise."

"How did you find out?" I wiped sweat from my brow. Was I perspiring from the temperature or from being found out?

"Last Saturday, I saw you both walk out of Bruegger's together." Sarah stepped around to the back of the cart where her golf bag was strapped in.

I followed her. "That's how you knew?"

"That, and your response just now." Sarah removed two irons and handed me one. "When did you two start dating?"

Was I having this conversation with Sarah?

"Last February. Kimberly is talking of moving in together while I'm still trying to figure out if I'm even a les—" As usual, I choked on the word. "She said 'I love you' after a month. How can anyone know so soon?"

"You either know or you don't. Has there ever been someone you couldn't stop thinking about?"

"What is this? The Spanish Inquisition?" Humor alert: nerves on fire.

"My advice is to do what makes your heart sing. Do you see yourself with Kimberly in five years?"

"No."

"If that's the case, why prolong it?"

"You're right. Maybe I should break up with her tonight." Not that I would even know what to say, but I was so used to following Sarah's suggestions that the response felt automatic.

"Whoa." Sarah clutched my forearm. My skin under her touch burned. Only when she removed her hand did it cool. "You've got to wait until orientation is over. I can't have a counselor with a broken heart. Kimberly's smart enough to figure out she'll never find another lover as outgoing and lovely as you."

Saddened as I was at the thought of ever breaking Kimberly's heart, I was thrilled to hear Sarah's opinion of me.

I pulled into Sarah's driveway and parked behind four shiny cars, each newer than my dad's hand-me-down Honda Accord. It was late July. Days earlier, as Sarah and I had begun packing up the office in preparation for the last orientation session, she'd invited me to her house for a dinner party, saying Linda wanted to meet me. Sarah had mentioned Linda over the summer, saying things like, "Last night, Linda and I saw a great movie." Or "Linda and I had dinner at such-and-such restaurant." I had assumed Linda was Sarah's partner, but she had never come out and said so, and I certainly wasn't going to ask. The only pictures on Sarah's desk were of cats.

Sarah and Linda's one-story cottage abutted a forest of trees that filtered the already dimming sunlight. Fall was approaching, as was, yet again, the real world, and the reminder I had no job, no plan, and no clue as to what my next step in it would be.

"I told you not to bring anything." Sarah opened the screen door. A gray-and-black striped cat slipped out, brushing my leg. Startled, I almost dropped the bowl of fruit.

"It might come as a shock to you." I handed her the bowl. "But yours is not the only advice I live by. My mother told me never to show up to a dinner party empty-handed."

I followed Sarah into a wide-open room divided by a long counter, with a small kitchen to the right and a larger living room to the left. Rachel, seated on a couch with two women I didn't recognize, turned and said hi. Piano music played in the background. Sarah put the bowl on the counter and introduced me to the woman in the kitchen who was adding cherry tomatoes to a salad.

"Sarah talks about you all the time." Linda's pale-yellow hair was cut in a short style akin to Sarah's. She wore a white polo shirt that exposed toned and tanned arms. After wiping her hand with a dishtowel, she extended it. I was surprised to find her grip weak. I'd assumed Sarah's girlfriend would have Sarah's same edge. Was the idiom "opposites attract" true for gay couples too?

"Sarah says you're an amazing golfer," I said. "Maybe we could all play."

"You're not ready to play with her quite yet." Sarah ushered me toward one of two matching club chairs framing a fireplace, across from the couch where Rachel and the two women were sitting. In the far corner were built-in shelves with a stereo on top, and books and CDs below. Sarah stood beside my chair and made introductions.

The two women beside Rachel were a couple. Nan, in the middle, was a head taller than both women and sported an auburn pixie cut with white at the temples. She smiled with her bright green eyes. Sarah said Nan taught history at Mount Holyoke College and had played professional basketball in a women's league in the seventies. Her girlfriend, Connie, was a psychotherapist in Hadley. She wore a violet dress, had a genuine smile, long, wavy honey-brown hair, and she was the only one there wearing makeup. The more I studied Nan and Connie, the more I wondered about opposites attracting. Could a significant age difference be considered an opposing characteristic?

A black-and-brown cat slinked near my leg. I dug my nails into the chair's armrests, bracing for a scratch.

Connie noticed my reaction. "Not a fan of cats?"

"It's more they're not a fan of me," I said. Sarah picked up the cat and cradled it in her arms.

"Sarah, the meat's ready." Linda placed a tray on the counter.

"Excuse me, ladies." Sarah put the cat on the other club chair, picked up the tray, and exited through a sliding glass door into a sunroom, pausing by a wicker chaise where a black cat lay curled. "You're being a good boy with all this company, aren't you, Izzy?" Sarah said in the cooing voice usually used with infants.

Sarah using a baby voice?

"So, where were we?" Linda lifted the cat from the chair and sat down, resting the cat on her lap.

"We were talking about who gets the house," said Connie. "They still haven't decided."

"Rumor is one wanted a child, the other didn't," Nan said. "They knew this from day one, but you remember when you first start dating. The sex haze blinds you from the important stuff."

Everyone laughed. Even me. I wasn't in on the joke, but I didn't want that to be obvious.

"Felice, Sarah says you have your first girlfriend." Linda stroked the cat's back. "How come she didn't come tonight?"

My face grew hot under the inquiry. "Tonight's the counselor hayride," I said. Rachel's bottom jaw went slack. Had she not known? I'd assumed Sarah had told her.

"I remember my first girlfriend," said Nan. "I was fifteen, and she was the swim coach."

"Nan!" Connie said.

"What? I was on the basketball team."

The women roared again. I stood. "May I use your bathroom?"

Linda pointed beyond the kitchen. Before the door closed behind me, I heard hushed voices.

"How old is she?"

"Twenty-three."

"She's a baby."

When I flicked on the light, I saw a bottle of White Musk. I opened the perfume bottle and was met with the familiar scent that each morning filled our office when Sarah arrived. I applied some on my wrists, then studied my reflection in the mirror. My hazel eyes looked greener thanks to my summer tan, and my thick eyebrows needed tweezing, but the real question, the one I'd been struggling with for months, remained: did I resemble the women (Rachel excluded) in the other room? Aside from sleeping with

Kimberly (I still didn't know if we were doing what lesbians were supposed to do), could I be a lesbian if I didn't have short hair and worship cats?

After dinner, Sarah escorted Rachel and me to the sandpile in her backyard to teach us how to chip a golf ball out of a bunker.

"Before this summer," I said, "I couldn't tell the difference between a nine iron and a curling iron."

"Sarah, phone call," Linda called from the porch. She left the cordless handset on the railing and went back inside.

"Be right back." Sarah handed me the wedge. "Practice."

"A girlfriend, huh?" Rachel said when Sarah was out of earshot. "How could you keep that from me? I thought I was your mentor."

"You are." I hadn't the heart to tell her she'd been replaced. "I'm not comfortable telling anyone."

"You told Sarah."

"Sarah guessed."

"What's up with you and Sarah?"

"What do you mean?" I looked across the yard. Sarah, phone to her head, was pacing on the porch, running her free hand through her hair.

"You two have this playfulness. Do you have a crush on her?"

"No." I maintained eye contact, but my flushed cheeks betrayed me. I'd never been a talented liar.

"Even if you do, forget it. Sarah and Linda have been together twelve years. You don't stand a chance."

"What do you have lined up after orientations end?" Linda asked me as we cleared dessert dishes from the sunroom.

"I'm moving home to start looking for a job." I placed the dishes on the kitchen counter. "What do you do?"

"I used to be a fourth-grade teacher, but now I'm a stay-at-home mom to the cats." As though to prove it, she emptied two cans of cat food onto two small saucers and placed them on the floor. Three cats materialized out of nowhere.

"How did you and Sarah meet?"

"My neighbor brought Sarah over one night. Sarah had walked right over to Izzy, my oldest and most finicky cat, and picked him up. Izzy didn't like anyone but when he snuggled into Sarah's arms, I knew she was the one."

"Because Sarah liked your cat?"

"No." Linda shook her head. "Because my cat liked Sarah."

I was the first to leave the dinner party. Sarah walked me outside, and we stood on the front steps admiring the stars, tiny pinpricks against the black sky. A breeze made me shiver. Sarah untied the white UMass sweatshirt from around her shoulders and draped it over mine. Inhaling her scent made me smile.

"Thanks. I'll bring it to work tomorrow."

"Keep it. I have plenty."

I stifled a grin. "I can't believe how fast this summer went by."

"And every summer they go faster." Sarah rocked back onto the heels of her loafers. "You still thinking of breaking up with Kimberly?"

"Yes. And she's still thinking of moving in together. Crazy, right?"

"What's crazy is buying a house together." Sarah planted her feet back down. "The couple they've been talking about tonight is the perfect example."

"Don't you and Linda own this house?" A breeze passed through, rustling the leaves. I pulled the sweatshirt tighter around my shoulders.

"No, I bought it before we met. It's perfect because my cats have a yard to roam around."

"How many cats do you have?" I spied a cream-colored cat with dark patches dart across the driveway.

"Five. But at one point I had ten."

"Ten?" I shouldn't have sounded shocked, but come on, ten? "Well, thanks again for dinner." I moved down one step. Sarah, thinking I was turning to hug her, leaned toward me, but since I was below her, she fell forward. I caught her, our faces inches apart. I thought she might kiss me. She didn't. Had I wanted her to? What would I have done if she had? With Kimberly it felt like I was testing the gay waters, could back out at any moment, claim I was still straight, phase over. But Sarah was the real deal. Would kissing her have more significance?

I helped Sarah regain her balance and hurried to my car. Once inside, I saw a gift I had forgotten I'd brought for Sarah. "Hey," I called out my open window. "I have something for you."

Sarah walked down the driveway, and I handed her a mix tape through the window. "This includes some of Kenny Loggins's recent songs, since you only play his old stuff."

"Are you implying my musical taste is outdated?"

"Well. . ."

"Bite me," Sarah said.

"Bite me? Guess I've rubbed off on you."

"More than you know." Sarah reached in and squeezed my shoulder. "WOFTOG."

"Woof what?" I asked, still reeling from her touch.

"WOFTOG. It stands for Watch. Out. For. The. Other. Guy," Sarah explained. "Like distracted drivers."

As I drove away, I saw Sarah in my rearview mirror, still there, watching me.

We held our end-of-summer banquet in the basement of Crabtree. Counselors had covered the concrete walls with poster-sized black-and-white photographs of orientation staffs from the last twenty-three years. I'd seen these photos during previous summers, but now I was looking at them in a new light. Standing in front of the most recent photo, taken that summer, I stared at Sarah's face. Then I scanned each photo going back in time, watching her grow younger until her first year: 1970, the summer she was thirty-four. The summer I was born. Sarah had the same haircut, the same smile. The only thing missing was the crow's feet. Strange to see her closer to my age than to her own present age. Was she as intimidating back then? Would I still have had a crush on her?

Across the room, Sarah was sitting with Peg, each with a plate of finger foods on their laps. Sarah, possibly sensing my stare, looked up and gave me that warm smile where her entire face lit up and made me feel as though I was just the person she wanted to see. Did she know I'd been studying her in the photos?

"Sarah looks so young." Kimberly appeared at my side. "But I'm sure she was every bit as tough."

"She's not that tough," I countered.

"To you, maybe. I can't wait until I never have to hear her tell me to be ten minutes early ever again."

I glanced back at Sarah, thinking how when orientations ended, so would my time with her.

In the first skit of the evening, two male counselors, wearing bathrobes, performed a mock campus tour in which their robes kept opening. Other male counselors, pretending to be female new students, shrieked in delight. The mood was festive and relaxed, the stress of preparing forty-five hundred students for the start of college now behind us.

Sarah ended the banquet by passing out her annual awards, which reflected funny events from the summer. The only difference this year was that Sarah handed them out from behind a waist-high dresser. Earlier in the evening she'd said to me, "I don't want to hug some of these counselors." She often adored her staff, but not that summer. A week earlier at lunch she'd said, "Where'd I go wrong? When I'd interviewed them, they sounded so smart."

"Perhaps they've eaten too much processed turkey." I'd lifted a slice of the grayish meat off my plate, having veered, mistakenly, from my regular tuna sandwich. "What are they trying to do, make me sick?" I'd said, mimicking Roseanne Roseannadanna.

Sarah had eased into a smile. "I can't stay mad with you around."

Which was why at the banquet I'd dragged a dresser to the front of the room to stand between Sarah and any potential hugs.

When the banquet ended, I went up to our office to change clothes. The staff was going on a ghost tour of campus led by a counselor whose knowledge of UMass history surpassed Sarah's. When my skirt hit the floor, the door opened.

"Brilliant idea with that dresser. I didn't want to hug anyone." Sarah closed the door behind her as I stepped into my jeans. "However, you, I'd hug."

Before I comprehended her words, Sarah had her arms around me. I put mine around her. The full length of our bodies touched, each part lining up. Her palms moved in little circles against my back. The familiar scent of her perfume warmed my insides. I closed my eyes. The hug transported me into another dimension, where seconds became minutes. Even though it was only a hug, its intensity made me feel I was being unfaithful to Kimberly.

"I've got to say." Sarah released me and stepped back, her blue eyes holding mine. "After doing this job for so many summers, you've made this one different from all the others."

"Uh," I stammered, not sure how to answer. "Everyone's waiting. I should get going,"

"Promise you won't be a stranger?" Sarah's expression was one I hadn't seen before, as though her feelings were dependent upon my answer.

"I promise," I said.

What's Next?
September 1993–December 1993

"I hate my dorm," my younger sister Jackie said to me over the phone. I was sitting on the floor of my childhood bedroom, encircled by piles of memorabilia. Our youngest sister, Meredith, was on my bed doing her sixth-grade math homework.

"But the rooms in Orchard Hill have magnificent views," I said. "They're high on a hill."

"Exactly. And I have to walk that hill every day. Why did you tell me to live here?" Jackie was right. When she'd come through orientation that summer, I'd persuaded her to choose that residential area, the exact opposite advice I'd given thousands of other new students. In my defense, Orchard Hill's reputation was studious, and my sister, though smart, was a partier, so I'd figured she'd be better off with fewer distractions.

"You can move next semester." I threw a handful of miniature Smurfs onto a giveaway pile. Meredith jumped off the bed, scooped up the blue figurines, and carted them to her room.

"My RA said it's rare you get to move," Jackie whined.

"Don't worry, I still have connections." I hung up and scanned the piles I'd created: college textbooks, photo albums of high school friends I'd lost touch with, jigsaw puzzles, and stacks of *The Daily Collegians* with my columns inside. What should I hold on to? What could I toss? Would any of it be useful for my future? And how did one even get from here to their future? The want ads? My dream was to be an opinion columnist, based on how much I'd loved writing for the *Collegian*, but I knew it wasn't a career easily attainable to a new graduate with no real-world experience. I would have to work my way up again. In the few weeks I'd been home, I'd mailed copies of my published columns to editors at the *Cape Cod Times*, the *Boston Globe* and several local papers in between. No one had responded with job offers—if they'd responded at all. I contemplated graduate school, but I wasn't keen on going back into a classroom just yet. I'd enjoyed the work I did in admissions—traveling, recruiting, running orientation, meeting new people, solving issues—but I had never considered it a career possibility, just a job that paid the rent while I pursued writing.

I applied to jobs in my major, public relations and sports marketing, with the Boston Celtics and Fox TV, where I'd had a month-long internship two years earlier. They'd both offered menial positions, a way in the door, but the commute it would require (considering they didn't pay enough to rent a place of my own) didn't seem worth it. Friends had relocated across the country and even gone overseas for jobs because they'd had no choice. I did. I didn't have to take any job. In fact, my dad had told me *not* to take any job just for the sake of having one, and had encouraged me to explore my interests. Even so, it didn't make the situation any less stressful.

September had always been a time for a fresh start, though now I wasn't sure how to go about starting it. With no reason to get up in the morning, I felt lost, a doer with nothing to do. I wished UMass had handed me an orientation packet for the real world after graduation, something to give me a little direction, just as they'd done when I'd arrived freshman year. Even a "what to expect when you graduate" flier letting graduates know that depression, confusion, and fear were all normal emotions after being flung from the safety net of college would've been useful.

A high school friend, also living at home, convinced me to join a local women's basketball league, which gave me something to do two nights a week. We played in middle school gyms across the Cape. At one game, a reporter who'd covered my high school athletic career, and who knew I wanted to be a writer, offered me a column in *The Cape Cod Sports Report*, his startup newspaper.

He called it "Felice's Focus" and said I could be creative but the column had to be sports related. My first piece was about my experience attending Larry Bird's basketball camp as a young girl and meeting my idol. It was great to have an outlet for my writing, though still not enough to stop me from worrying that my best days were behind me. And when I worried, I turned to one person.

"What's up?" Uncle Mark said when I called, the sounds of his fingers dancing across a calculator in the background. He was a comptroller at a Manhattan advertising agency that designed posters for Lincoln Center.

"I wake up every day with a pit in my stomach because I have no idea what I should be doing."

"Come visit me. See if you could live here. A lot of writers do."

"But New York City's huge." I was lying on my bed, staring up at the glow stars my dad and I had stuck to the ceiling on my fourteenth birthday.

"You said the same thing about UMass and look what you accomplished. Let go of your to-do list for one minute. I can get us tickets to *Les Mis*."

"Okay." Sorting through the piles of my past could wait.

I woke the next morning without stomach pains; I had somewhere to be. I drove west under a cloudless and vibrant blue sky, radio blaring. As I approached the exit that would take me south to New York City, Kenny Loggins's song "I'm Alright" came on. It was the theme song from *Caddyshack*, one of Sarah's favorite movies because it was about golf. Was it a sign? And if so, what did that mean? Only one way to find out. I shut off my turn signal, turned up the radio, and continued heading toward Amherst. Something, or perhaps someone, was calling me back.

Two hours later I was on the UMass campus, climbing the admissions building's fire escape. On the third-level landing, I peeked through Sarah's window. The jar of beans, its red bow faded, remained on the windowsill. I knocked on the glass. Sarah, seated at her round table, looked up at me over her reading glasses. Her shocked expression eased into a smile, relieving me of the angst that perhaps my detour had been a mistake.

Sarah opened the emergency-exit door, which, to my surprise, didn't set off an alarm. "What are you doing here?"

"Thought I'd surprise you. I know how much you love surprises."

"In your case, I'll make an exception." She hugged me, reigniting those thoughts I'd had during that hug we'd shared two months earlier. "I almost called to see if you were around to go to a movie but figured you were busy."

She'd wanted to call me for a movie!

Piano music was playing when we entered her office and sat across from each other. It struck me as funny to be sitting there causally, as I remembered how I'd felt the first time I'd sat there on my interview two years before—rigid with nerves.

"How've you been?" Sarah asked.

"I'm freaking out since the real world is here, and I seem to be the only one of my friends with no idea of what I should be doing. I know I have options, and I don't want to sound ungrateful, but it's overwhelming. Everyone seems to have a purpose except for me. I feel this constant pressure not to make any wrong decisions that'll set me on the wrong course for life."

"What do we tell incoming freshmen about choosing their majors?"

"That it's okay to switch."

"Exactly," Sarah said. "And that advice holds true after you graduate. Whatever you start today, you can start something else tomorrow."

"But I don't know where *to* start." I cringed at my tone, the No Whining sign in my peripheral vision.

"Felice, you're not the traditional graduate. You want to write, and it might take longer to reach that goal, but you'll achieve everything you put your mind to. Everyone's journey is different."

"What did you do after you graduated?"

"I worked for the Girl Scouts. When a director position opened that required a master's degree, I came to UMass to get one. My degree required revamping new students' orientation, which I did by applying what I learned from the Girl Scouts." That explained why some new students who came through orientation said it felt like camp. "And the same month I received my degree, the director position became available here, and I got it. I never dreamed I'd be at UMass twenty-three years."

"That's how long I've been alive."

"Don't remind me." Sarah huffed.

"I just wish I had some direction. Living at home feels like a lapse in my job progress. Plus, I miss Amherst, the restaurants, the hiking trails. Would you believe I even miss the stench of cow manure?"

Sarah chuckled. "Ever been to the Summit House at the top of Skinner Mountain? I'd love to take you."

Did she mean it? Were we making plans? Would Linda come?

"Cool." I tried to mask my enthusiasm.

"How's your sister adjusting?"

"She loves school, but hates her dorm and wants to move to Southwest. I feel bad since I told her to live in Orchard Hill."

Sarah tilted her head. "I seem to remember you sitting in that seat saying new students shouldn't take advice from older siblings."

"I know, but she's my sister. I'm protective."

"Let me make a call." Sarah picked up the phone, and I went to use the bathroom, stopping to say hi to Peg. When I reentered Sarah's office, she'd secured a new room for Jackie for the spring semester.

"So." Sarah leaned back in her chair. "Are you in town to see Kimberly?"

I shook my head. "She doesn't know I'm here. I was on my way to New York City to see if I could live there, since it will be easier to get a job that pays the rent, which everyone says I'll need."

"What jobs are you considering?"

"I saw a woman on TV who organizes closets in Manhattan. I've organized plenty of dorm rooms. I was thinking I'd call her."

"My bedroom closet could use help. If you're available tonight, I'll hire you."

"Are you serious?"

"Absolutely. And you're welcome to stay over. I have a guest room."

"You don't mind?"

"Why would I mind?" Sarah smiled. "You'll be working magic

on my closet."

I called Mark, told him I'd see him tomorrow, and gave him Sarah's home number. Then I called Jackie to tell her that Sarah got her a new dorm room for the spring.

"I'm meeting folks for lunch." Sarah was standing by the door when I hung up. "Join us."

Rachel was munching fried wonton strips and jumped up to give me a hug. I sat between her and Brenda, the director of Parking Services, at a table inside Panda East. Brenda resembled a snowman—round head atop round middle. She was who had called Sarah two years earlier when I'd been overzealous in my attempt to get a parking sticker, which had led to the jar of beans and to making Sarah laugh. I considered thanking her.

"Felice used to be a columnist for the *Collegian.*" Sarah sat directly across from me. "Do you remember that article on George Bush's aversion to broccoli?" I smiled despite Sarah saying "used to," as though my life would now be about things I "used to" do.

"Do you have a writing job?" asked the director of Career Services. She was dressed in shades of red—dark-red sweater, pale-red shirt, cherry-red pants.

"Yes. For a small paper on Cape Cod."

"Felice also works as an organizer," Sarah said. "I've hired her to organize my closet."

"She did an amazing job organizing the supplies in the Alumni Office." Rachel looked at me. "And didn't you get extra credit for organizing the office at the Volleyball Hall of Fame in Holyoke?"

I nodded.

"How did you become good at organizing?" asked Brenda.

"I grew up with two walk-in closets that were great practice."

"My closets need you," Brenda said. "Can I get your number?"

I caught Sarah's eye and she winked at me.

Our waiter came by to tell us the special was soft-shell crabs with garlic sauce.

"I'll have that." Sarah handed the waiter her menu. "Except with the bean sauce."

"I bet Linda will be thankful." I remembered our staff lunch over the summer, when Sarah had ordered the same dish with garlic, saying sarcastically, “Linda’s going to love this.”

“She left today for California.” Sarah lifted the white teapot and refilled her cup.

“Her annual family trip?” asked Rachel. Sarah nodded. But that didn’t add up. If Linda was away, why hadn’t Sarah ordered the garlic sauce? Was it because I was coming over? I looked across the table and found Sarah smiling at me. A strange nervousness took hold. The thought of being in her house with her alone scared and delighted me.

“A toast to Felice.” Sarah raised her teacup. “The best night director we ever had.”

“Do I get credit for finding her?” Rachel lifted her cup.

“You sure do.” Sarah’s gaze remained on me as though no one else was there.

“Guess what?” I pulled a tiny white slip of paper from my pocket. “This was my fortune today at Panda. ‘Your help will be needed in an embarrassing situation.’ Guess we found the embarrassing situation.”

Sarah and I were standing inside her long and narrow walk-in closet. Shirts and pants were hung with no sense of order, and the shelf above it was covered with sweaters in the same disarray.

“You won’t tell anyone, will you?” Sarah feigned mortification.

“Don’t worry. An organizer is like a doctor: client-organizer confidentiality.” I pointed to a short plastic shelf unit stuffed with hand towels. “What are these for?”

“The cat that sleeps in the closet.”

“What does he do with them? Dust?”

Sarah laughed. “I wish. We use them to clean up his messes.”

“And in there?” I gestured to a short file cabinet in the corner.

“Important house documents.”

Just then, a fat, woolly orange cat leapt out from behind the cabinet, sending dust bunnies scattering as though afraid of being caught. I yelped and jumped back. Sarah picked up the cat and held her face next to his.

Getting that near a cat? No, thank you.

“You scared your Auntie Felice, didn’t you, Sammy?” Sarah spoke in the same baby voice she’d used the night of her party.

"Your cat lives in the closet? Is he gay?"

"Like you, he's not sure. He goes in and out all day."

"Ha, ha," I said. "You're hilarious."

We piled the contents of Sarah and Linda's closet onto their queen-sized bed, and then I lined up their shoes, in pairs, along the wall. Sarah kept telling me to slow down, but when I organized I had only one speed.

I'd been nervous entering Sarah's bedroom. Would I find accoutrements like the ones I'd seen on the fliers at Our Hideaway? Or were those hidden in the file cabinet along with the deed to the house? Turns out, their bedroom was as nondescript as any other: Scenic pictures of gardens and landscapes on the walls, books on the nightstand, and a long dresser with a television on one end and a cluster of framed photos of Sarah and Linda on the other.

While Sarah vacuumed the closet, I divided the clothing into categorized piles on the bed: work, casual, golf, and donate.

"I need one for soft clothes," Sarah said when I'd pointed out the piles.

"What clothes?"

"Soft clothes. They're what I wear around the house."

"But there's casual." I nodded to a heap of colorful tops.

"Soft clothes are more worn out."

"Like this one?" I lifted a rose-colored sweater with huge shoulder pads from the donate pile.

"I still wear that." Sarah reached for it.

"While you were vacuuming, the eighties called and asked for it back."

"First you imply my music is outdated, and now my clothes?" Sarah tossed the sweater back onto the donate pile. "Bite me."

"Be careful what you ask for," I replied. Sarah's eyes became dinner plates. Didn't she know I was teasing? During the summer we had developed our own banter, even Rachel had noticed it, but maybe I'd crossed a line with too sexual an innuendo. Allowing someone into your closet—your personal space—can create a more intimate connection. Sarah's welcoming me into hers had changed our relationship once again. Where we stood now, however, I had no idea.

"When's the last time you cleaned out your closet?" I hoped by switching topics she'd forget my remark.

"Not for years."

"Since we don't remember everything we have, every year we should take it all out and get rid of what doesn't fit or is out of fashion. Think of it as cleaning out the past and making room for the future. The fun part is putting it back together."

"Easy for you to say. You love puzzles."

"No worries. I'll put it all back. You just choose what to donate."

A scratching sound came from the front door. Sarah walked out to open it and three cats sauntered in, tails up as though on parade.

"Dinner's ready, boys," she said. They really were her kids.

An hour later we put two bags of clothing into Sarah's car for donation. While she prepared dinner, I put everything back in the closet by style and color. The item I saved for last was the teal cotton sweater Sarah had worn at the end-of-the-summer banquet. I brought it to my nose and her scent triggered the memory of that hug. I could almost feel her body against mine. When I heard footsteps, I tossed the sweater up onto the shelf.

"The closet looks amazing." Sarah patted my lower back, sending goosebumps up my spine. "Wait till Linda sees this."

We walked into the kitchen and Sarah offered me wine.

"No thanks." I sat at the counter. "One sip and I'd be drunk."

"Cheap date." Sarah's response was the type of suggestive banter that led to thoughts of us doing suggestive things. But it was just flirting.

Truthfully, I'd had no experience or understanding of the danger in flirting with someone who had a partner. How naïve I'd been to think that factor could keep anything from happening between two people. Aside from the dream I'd had of Sarah kissing me, I hadn't dreamt beyond that. Beyond was unchartered territory. Beyond was real. Beyond was, I knew, wrong. But beyond also enticed me to no end.

Sarah sat beside me and opened her checkbook. Touching her chest for her reading glasses and, not finding them, she touched the top of her head, then brought her glasses down to her nose. "Shall I write the check out to Felice?"

"Make it out to Closet Queen."

"For real?" Sarah peered over her rims at me. Her gaze was maternal and comforting but also made her look smart and sexy.

"No."

"Oh, but I love it." She handed me a check for one-hundred dollars, far more than I'd calculated. "It includes a tip," Sarah added. "You're worth every penny."

"Thanks." The knots in my stomach linked to my diminishing bank account loosened. "Maybe I should consider organizing until I find a writing job."

"Why not? You're incredible at creating order, whether with closets or an office. Amazing how your brain works under all those curls." Sarah ruffled my hair as she returned to the stove.

"Do you think people would assume I'm just a cleaning lady?"

"Who cares what people think? Organizing can be a job, not your career. You can still be a writer." Sarah shut off the stove and began spooning food onto two plates. "Do me a favor. Grab placemats from the linen closet. It's just outside the bathroom."

As I removed the placemats, a blue-and-white toiletry bag fell to the floor. I stuffed the bag back inside. "This closet could use work too."

"I know," said Sarah. "Don't think your work here is done."

After dinner, we read the *Daily Hampshire Gazette* and *USA Today* in the living room. Sarah sat in a club chair with Sammy on her lap. I sat on the couch, eyeing a gray-and-black striped cat beside me, bracing myself for his sudden movements. When the phone rang, Sarah chatted with the caller, then tossed me the cordless phone. "Your uncle."

"Kimberly called looking for you," Mark said. "I told her you were in the bathroom. Wasn't sure what you told her."

"Thanks." I hung up and called Kimberly.

"How's New York?" asked Kimberly.

"New York's great," I said. Sarah lowered her newspaper and looked at me.

"If you're stopping in Amherst on Sunday, want to meet in Northampton?" Kimberly asked.

"Sure," I said, meeting Sarah's gaze.

"Great. I love you."

"Uh-huh." My standard response whenever Kimberly said those three words.

"Everything okay?" Sarah asked when I hung up.

"I feel bad when Kimberly says she loves me because I don't say it back. I don't think I'll ever say it to anyone."

"You will when it's the right person."

The familiar scratching noise sounded again from the front door. The cats' doorbell. Sarah let the cats in and looked at her watch. "Eleven? We'd better get to sleep."

The guest room was just off the living room. Inside was an open steamer trunk filled with packages of peanut-butter crackers, AAA batteries, and paper towels. Sarah, ever the Girl Scout, was always prepared. At the far end of the room was an itchy-looking black-and-white-checkered wool couch.

"It's freezing in here." I shivered. Fall in Western Massachusetts had warm days and chilly nights.

"This room used to be a garage, but we never got around to insulating it." Sarah removed a couch cushion.

"And you have the nerve to call it a guest room? It's more an ice room."

"When we have guests, we warm it beforehand with a portable heater, which I forgot to do." Sarah held the cushion to her chest as though it were a shield. "Maybe you should sleep in my bed."

Sleep in her bed? With her? Had she only offered to be nice and didn't really want me in her bed? Or had she not heated the room on purpose because she did want me in her bed? This scenario had never crossed my mind.

In the bathroom I felt nervous as I brushed my teeth, removed my contact lenses, and changed into pajamas. Then I stood in the doorway of Sarah's bedroom—as I'd once stood in her office doorway—unsure if I should enter.

"You might as well come in." Sarah was already in bed, the television airing The Weather Channel.

I slipped under the covers beside her as the phone rang. Sarah swept back the blanket, grabbed the phone from the nightstand, and walked out saying, "Hi, Linda. Wait until you see our closet."

Ten minutes later Sarah was back in bed.

"How's Linda?" I asked.

"Fine."

"My feet are freezing."

"Put them near the cats." Sarah was referring to the two lying between us.

"Will the cats scratch me through the blanket?" I asked, instead of the question I really wanted to ask: Would the cats sleep here all night?

"Don't worry. Put them next to mine, you'll be fine."

I did. Our feet touched. Sarah shut off the TV.

"I don't think Linda likes me," I said, emboldened by the darkness. "I got this vibe from her at your dinner party."

"Of course she does. But for the record, you slept in the guest room."

When Sarah's alarm clock chimed the next morning, I woke burrowed against her backside. In my sleep, I must've assumed she was Kimberly. Sarah reached over her head to the shelf, tapped the alarm off, and as she retracted her hand, pressed her palm to my head. The touch lasted only a second, but tenderness emanated through her fingertips. I pretended to be asleep. Sarah got out of bed and moved through what I assumed was her morning ritual: making coffee, feeding cats, taking a shower. At some point I fell back asleep.

"Hey, sleepyhead." Sarah touched my leg. I opened my eyes. Sarah, standing beside the bed, was dressed for work. "I'm leaving but stay as long as you want. There's food in the fridge; help yourself. I left a list of which cats you can let out before you leave." She sounded nervous. I'd never seen her nervous. Was it because she'd found me cuddled against her?

"Thanks again for letting me sleep over." I sat up, unsure if I should get out of bed and hug her.

"Thanks for organizing my closet. If you have time when you come back, perhaps we can grab dinner."

Dinner!

"Sure."

"Remember, WOFTOG," Sarah said before leaving. I watched through the window as her car retreated down the driveway. Then

I hopped out of bed, made it, let out the designated cats, taped a thank-you note to her toothbrush, and beamed the entire drive to the Bronx.

"AIDS is my biggest fear," Uncle Mark said that night, the two of us on his couch, huddled under a blanket. We'd just watched the movie *And the Band Played On*.

"But you use condoms, don't you?" At UMass, safe sex had been drummed into my head.

"Yes. But was there a time or two I didn't?" He aimed the remote at the television and began flipping channels.

"Why would you risk it?"

"Sometimes you get caught up, you know?"

I didn't know. He settled on ESPN. As he watched the Yankees highlights, I told him I had a crush on Sarah.

Without looking at me he asked, "Is she single?"

"She has a girlfriend."

"Was the girlfriend home?"

"No."

That got his attention. Mark muted the television and looked at me. "Where did you sleep?"

"The guest room was the plan, but it was cold and—"

"Felice, did you sleep in the same bed with your ex-boss?"

"Yes, but—"

"No buts." He shook his head. "Just be careful."

The next morning Mark and I each read a different Dean Koontz paperback on the crowded subway down to Forty-Second Street. After scrambling through commuters and tourists we entered his shiny high-rise building. His twenty-sixth-floor office had a breathtaking view of Times Square. Mark scribbled a map of Midtown on the back of a business envelope, and off I went.

On the streets, throngs of people stared ahead as though in a mass trance. No one smiled. No one gazed up at the architecture; they just moved, stopping at red signals, walking at white ones. I marveled they weren't bumping into one another.

I headed down Fifth Avenue, surprised that my natural stride matched the hurried pace of New Yorkers. At Madison Square

Park, I sat in view of the Flatiron Building, fascinated by how the two sides came together at a curved point. Surrounded by trees and overshadowed by buildings, I felt comfortable in that urban jungle. Maybe this Muppet could take Manhattan.

I wrote in my journal about my evening with Sarah. The flirting as we sorted clothes, the intimacy of sleeping together, and waking up spooned against her. No wonder she seemed nervous; I'm sure she thought it had been a mistake to let me sleep in her bed. She was probably aware of my crush. Perhaps Linda detected it too and that's why I got the sense she didn't like me. Did she fear I might steal Sarah?

Ha! Who was I to think I had such sway over someone like Sarah? Though I had to admit, watching her teeter around her house in scuffed slippers was the equivalent to peering behind Oz's curtain and seeing underneath the great and powerful exterior. Something had shifted. I no longer feared her.

As I headed back uptown, I passed a golf store and saw a club in the window like the one Sarah had said she wanted. Back at my uncle's office, I called her.

"Sarah." She answered her direct line in her direct way.

"Hi, it's Felice."

"I was just thinking of you." Her voice grew animated. "I'm listening to the Kenny tape you made me."

She was thinking of me!

I described the club. It wasn't the same one, but Sarah appreciated my looking out for her.

"Are you still planning on stopping in Amherst on Sunday?"

"Yes." I stared out the window, mesmerized by the flashing lights touting Broadway shows.

"Will you be staying with Kimberly?"

"Not sure."

"You're welcome to sleep over again."

My eyes rested on the giant MTV sign. "You don't mind?"

"Not at all," Sarah said.

Mark and I met up with Steven, his boyfriend of three months, for dinner. Steven, Mark had told me, worked in fashion, and used to oversee the Macy's Thanksgiving Day Parade. Steven was the same height as my uncle, wore a navy pin-striped suit with a pink tie that matched his pink socks, and was in his late fifties, twenty years older than Mark. His thinning white hair was in stark contrast to Mark's full head of black hair. In greeting, Steven kissed Mark on the lips. I'd never seen my uncle kiss anyone, even his college girlfriend. Despite my embarrassment observing others' displays of affection, I was pleased to see Mark content.

After dinner we attended services at a gay and lesbian synagogue in the West Village.

"Everyone looks similar to the people at the Cape Cod Synagogue," I whispered to Mark. "Like, normal."

"Imagine that," he replied.

"What do you think?" Mark asked early the next morning as we walked the loop in Van Cortlandt Park, CUNY college track runners in their colorful jerseys lapping us. "Could you live here?"

"Not sure. In New York, you're constantly checking that you've still got your wallet. But it might be good to live somewhere with no ties." I stared into the forest that bordered the path, amazed, as always, this was the Bronx. Trees weren't necessarily what one thought of when they thought of this borough. "Speaking of ties, I need to break up with Kimberly."

"Because of Sarah?"

Was it?

"No. I've wanted to do it for months, just haven't known what to say. I don't want to hurt her."

"Alright." Mark picked up an acorn and chucked it into the woods. "This is what you're going to say."

Sitting in my parked car, I stared at the Hestia Mural painted on the side of a downtown Northampton building. It illustrated images of women from the last three centuries, including Sojourner Truth, sewing, farming, and teaching. No wonder Northampton was teeming with lesbians; the town itself seemed to have a veiled preference for women.

After rehearsing the words Mark had helped me put together, I walked up to Main Street. Kimberly was standing in front of the Academy of Music and ran over when she saw me.

"I've missed you." She hugged me. I stiffened because we were in public and because of my news. "How was New York? Are you going to move there?"

"Haven't decided."

We walked onto the Smith College campus, cutting through a cluster of ivy-covered brick buildings that led to colorful gardens and a pond framed by emerald-green athletic fields. Ducks drifted in a V-formation along the water.

Feeling my confidence begin to crumble, I blurted, "I need to end us. You deserve a girlfriend who can love you as much as you love her, not someone confused with her sexuality."

Kimberly gasped. "Why?"

"Because it's your senior year. You should enjoy it without my issues."

"I don't want someone else. Why can't we enjoy it together?"

"Because it's not my life anymore." I swept my arm across the collegiate landscape to sharpen my point.

"What can I do to change your mind?" Mark had warned me Kimberly might say that. He'd also said it wasn't fair to be with her when I didn't love her and to remember the times we'd slept together, which hadn't revved me up half as much as when Sarah had hugged me. Not that I thought I had a chance with Sarah, but he'd assured me someone was out there who'd make me feel similarly excited.

"Nothing. It's not you, it's me." How unoriginal but how correct that trite phrase was.

"Is this because I told Evan about us?"

"You did what?" Having Evan, my former counselor, think I was gay when I wasn't even sure I was, emboldened my decision.

"I needed to share us with someone." She rested her hand on my thigh. A pack of women in Smith College T-shirts jogged by and I slid my leg away, her hand slipping off.

"Kimberly, you deserve a girlfriend who's comfortable with you telling your friends."

"But I don't have to tell anyone else."

"That's not fair to you."

"How come you're not sad?" A tear slid down her cheek.

"I am sad. This isn't easy for me."

"But you're not even crying."

"You know I'm not a crier. Plus, we'll still be friends."

"I can't be friends with you right now." Kimberly ran the back of her sleeve across her cheek. The last thing I wanted was to lose her friendship. Sarah said most lesbian couples remained friends after a breakup. I hoped in time that would prove true with us too.

My sister Jackie opened the front door of her residence hall wearing pajamas, despite it being early afternoon. I handed her a bag of bagels from New York. She pulled one out and bit into it. "So good. The bagels in the dining commons are not real bagels."

Up in Jackie's room I rearranged the two desks, two dressers, and two twin beds to give her and her roommate more space. When Jackie went downstairs to throw in a load of laundry, I called Sarah.

"I was hoping to hear from you," Sarah said. "How about dinner? My treat for organizing my closet." Sarah gave me directions to Fedora's Tavern in South Hadley, and we planned to meet at five. I hung up as Jackie walked back in. She saw my expression and asked what was so funny.

"Nothing," I said. Nerves, I thought.

Fedora's had multiple TVs airing football and baseball games, and most of the tables were filled with people eating chicken wings and cheering on their teams. I found Sarah seated in the back. She flashed a big smile when she saw me and stood up for a hug. Something stirred within me as our bodies connected. I enjoyed the sensation, but knew nothing could happen, if for no other reason than Sarah had a partner and therefore this couldn't go any further. Truthfully, I wasn't sure if I wanted it to. I enjoyed having a crush, and reveled in having her attention. It felt special. It felt like enough.

Sarah asked me to tell her everything I'd done since leaving her place days earlier. I was surprised she cared. I ended my itinerary with my breakup with Kimberly and how she'd said she couldn't be friends for a while.

"That's typical." Sarah unfolded her napkin and placed it on her lap. "But she'll come around."

I reached for my water; my throat suddenly dry from the question I was about to ask. "Is it okay if I stay over again?"

Sarah grinned. "Are you kidding?"

Back at Sarah's we read the Sunday *New York Times*, seated in the same positions as last time: Sarah in a chair, me on the couch, with jazz playing on the stereo and cats meandering around. It reminded me of how my parents enjoyed their Sunday afternoons, minus the cats.

Every few minutes one of us reported funny or newsworthy things we'd read. At one point I got up to show Sarah a picture of Tiger Woods's golf swing. Instead of returning to the couch, I sat on the floor beside her chair. Cat hair be damned.

"Listen to this." Sarah tapped my head as she read from an article. Even though sitting on the floor hurt my back, that tap made it worth it.

After the second tap, Sarah began caressing my scalp. A woozy stirring whizzed through me, like when I'd played spin the bottle at parties and my bottle had stopped with its neck pointing to a boy I liked. I willed myself not to move, which would've been easier had a black-and-brown cat not begun slinking around me like a vulture contemplating roadkill.

"You love your Auntie Felice, don't you, Maxi?" Sarah said. Scratching on the front door caused Sarah's hand to disappear from my head as she got up to let in more cats. "It's getting late. We should get to sleep."

"Did you turn on the space heater in the guest room?" I asked.

"Shit. I knew I forgot something."

I changed into pajamas in the bathroom. When I entered Sarah's bedroom, she was placing her next day's outfit—yellow sweater, white polo, khakis—on the dresser. Once in bed, the two of us on our backs, inches apart, Sarah shut off the lamp. The only light was a faint glow from the clock on the cable box. One second passed. Maybe two. And then.

"I don't know what to do about this crush I have on you," Sarah said. "I've had it since the day you interviewed to be a counselor."

Wait. What? That had been over two years ago. I felt speechless.

"I think it had to do with your pink sneakers." Sarah slid her left arm under my neck. As if I'd expected this or, better yet, had done it a thousand times, I turned onto my side, rested my head on her shoulder, and draped my arm around her. Sarah's body felt different from Kimberly's. Her muscles were softer, bones more pronounced, yet her motions confident. I melted into her.

"I want to kiss you and make love to you." Sarah wrapped her other arm around me. "But I can't because of Linda."

Linda! How had I totally forgotten about Linda? I was lying on her side of the bed for goodness' sake. While I agreed with Sarah's restrictions on kissing and making love, cuddling didn't seem as illicit, so I pushed away thoughts of Linda and focused instead on how I felt, which was content and happy. I didn't realize I was learning how to fulfill my desires and dodge guilt simply by justifying my actions. Separating what felt right from what was right would, in time, become second nature.

Sarah asked, "How do you feel?"

"Scared."

"Maybe we should stop." Her arms loosened around me.

"No." I held on tighter. "I don't want to stop."

"But I don't want you to be scared."

"I'm only scared of how good this feels."

Sarah sighed. "This is crazy."

"Yes, but you only live once, right? Though you live with it for life." When had I gotten so bold?

As we lay together, stillness overtook me, as though this was right where I should be. None of the past conundrums with other partners—wondering what they were thinking, what I should say, or how I should act—troubled me. As incredible as this moment felt, guilt still ate at me, thinking of how hurt Linda would be if she found out. Despite my remorse, however, I never wanted Sarah to let me go.

I woke early, on the edge of the bed, far from Sarah. She was on her side, her back to me. Had I dreamt the entire thing? A cream-colored cat with a brown patch on one half of his face lay curled between us. I inched closer to Sarah. The cat, Cody I think, stuck out his paws and arched his back into a downward stretch. I shielded my face with the blanket, thinking he might attack, but he just stepped over my legs to let me pass. I snuggled up to Sarah, fearful she might tell me the whole incident had been a mistake, but she reached back and rested her hand on my head. Her soft touch confirmed everything. We remained in that position until her alarm buzzed.

"I am the boss." Sarah shut it off and rolled onto her back. "I'll say I'm not feeling well."

I once again rested my head on her shoulder as she wrapped her arm around me. She turned on the television as President Bill Clinton, Israeli Prime Minister Yitzhak Rabin, and PLO Chairman Yasser Arafat were signing a first-ever peace treaty.

"A historic moment." Sarah's two meanings obvious.

At 8:30 a.m., Sarah, who never took a sick day, called the office.

"Best you stay in bed." Peg's southern accent sailed out of the earpiece. "No need catchin' somethin' that might catch ya first."

Sarah hung up, put on her bathrobe, and went into the kitchen to feed the cats. "Good morning, boys."

I went into the bathroom and brushed my teeth. We had yet to kiss, but I wasn't taking any chances. When I entered the kitchen, Sarah nuzzled her face into my neck. "You always smell so good. It makes me crazy. What perfume is it?"

"Jovan Musk."

Sarah took my face in her hands and stared into my eyes as though asking for permission. I smiled back, granting it. She brought her lips to mine and the sensation reached to my knees. Sarah's lips were thin, unlike Kimberly's, which were a suppler plum, but Sarah's lips were more disciplined. I could sense their intentionality and commitment to the kiss and not simply the abandonment to passion. Something was exchanged in that kiss. Something I wouldn't realize until much later and would be impossible to get back. My heart.

Sarah took my hand and led me into the bedroom.

I could've stopped. I could've said no. But I hadn't wanted to. All I'd wanted was to follow Sarah. I would've followed her anywhere. I hadn't had even an inkling that the repercussions from this moment would remain with me for decades. That despite how happy I'd be, heartache would follow. Had I known, would I have stopped? No. I would've still happily trailed Sarah into that bedroom because I'd been lost, and Sarah had been the only one offering direction.

We lay on our sides on top of the covers, dressed, limbs entwined. I'd heard of magnetic attraction but had never experienced it until then. I understood what Mark had meant about getting caught up in the moment. Nothing more than kissing was happening, but if it were to have happened, I didn't think I could've stopped myself. For the first time, I was not being guided by my brain. Every inch of my skin was yelling, "More!"

Sarah's lips separated from mine. "Do you think you can handle this?"

"Sure." What was there to handle? Cuddling? Kissing? I didn't see what we were doing as anything as bad as sleeping together, which, in my inexperienced mind, felt like the ultimate cheating maneuver. Despite the months of attraction, our brief interlude felt more spontaneous than long lasting, and I thought it certainly wouldn't compete with Sarah and Linda's dozen years together. Instead of picturing Linda being upset if she found out, I invented a lover for her, therefore making her relieved to have a way out of the relationship. I was desperate, trying any way to allay my guilt.

"When I looked at you across the table at Panda last week, I hoped the others couldn't tell what I was thinking," Sarah said. "Especially Rachel." Rachel already suspected I had a special fascination with Sarah. I dared not think of how she'd respond if she found out the feelings between me and Sarah were mutual.

"Speaking of Rachel. She and I and my sister are seeing Livingston Taylor in two weeks at the Iron Horse. Want to join us?" My only thoughts were immediate: when would I see Sarah again? I wasn't thinking about a commitment, or about starting down some path together, or even that our actions were causing her to cheat on Linda. I was just caught up in the emotions coursing through my body.

"I'd love to."

"Great. And Linda can come too." I wanted Sarah to reject the suggestion, which sent guilt again sparking through me. Was Sarah feeling any guilt?

"She'll still be in California."

"In that case, can I sleep over again?"

"You better." Sarah brushed a lock of hair from my face. "You know this will have to be our little secret."

Of course, I knew. And I was okay with that. It's how I'd handled every relationship.

"You remember the Rita Mae Brown book of poems *Songs to a Handsome Woman* you loaned me last summer?" I asked.

"Yes." Sarah weaved her fingers through mine.

"There was a Post-it on a poem about age differences between lovers. Did you do that on purpose?"

Sarah sighed. "I don't know what I was thinking. I should've had more restraint. There's just something about you. Promise me if you meet someone next week, you won't let me keep you from falling in love."

I promised. How hard could that be?

"Saw the pile of sweatshirts on your bedroom floor." Dad cut into his roast chicken that evening at dinner. "My guess is you spent as much at the bookstore as we paid in tuition."

"I got them for free when I worked in the alumni office," I said.

"Can I have the white one?" Meredith asked. That was the sweatshirt Sarah had given me the night of her dinner party. No way was I parting with it now.

"I have a blue one you'll like better."

"Yay!" Meredith shoveled peas onto her spoon with her thumb. She still held the innocence of girlhood, real-life decisions far ahead. I envied her. Moving home, with a year of work under my belt, felt as if I'd somehow failed at life.

"Tell everyone what happened tonight at karate," Dad said.

With her mouth full of peas, Meredith said, "I broke a board with my foot."

"Isn't that dangerous?" Mom grew up playing stoopball in Brooklyn, only ever touching her palm to a tiny rubber ball, so having daughters who played contact sports made her worry.

"Sarah says it's important for women to defend themselves," I said.

"I'm a girl," stated Meredith in a know-it-all tone.

"Even more reason," I told her.

"How did your spelling test go?" Mom asked Meredith. Despite everything Mom had going on, she always remembered our tests, athletic games, and other activities. Her memory for detail was what had attracted my dad when he'd been a psychology grad student at Yeshiva University in Manhattan. One day, when he'd been doing a study on short-term memory at Brooklyn College, he'd given each participant in the study a list to memorize. Mom, a senior, had been part of the study. One week later he'd called each student to check his or her temporary recall, and Mom had remembered the most of anyone. It was because of her memory, Dad would say, and not, he swore, because she was stunning, that he'd asked her out. Three months later they were engaged.

"I got a hundred," said Meredith.

"That's great," Dad told her, then looked at me. "Thought any more about getting a master's degree?"

Couldn't we just talk about the Patriots like a typical New England family?

With my fork, I speared a piece of chicken. "I was thinking of sports management, but Sarah says to do what makes my heart sing."

"I agree with Sarah," Mom said. "Does sports management do that for you?" It didn't, but I feared admitting I wanted to be a writer after they'd paid my tuition for a different major. That's when Sarah's voice appeared in my head: "Suck it up."

"I was thinking of giving writing a shot. I'm writing a column for Frank's paper, and Papa's experiences from the war."

"Sounds like a plan," Dad said. "We support anything you choose."

"It's your time to do what makes you happy," added Mom. But would they still support me if they knew what made me happy was Sarah?

"Are you crying?" Meredith asked.

"What's wrong, honey?" Mom reached for my hand.

"I'm sure you think I should get a job and move out." The tears were not entirely about my uncertain future career prospects, but about my Sarah secret. I hadn't told them I might be gay because I wasn't sure myself. And going from "I might be gay" to "I'm secretly hooking up with my ex-boss who is older than they are and has a long-term partner" didn't sound like a smart way to introduce the discussion. Besides, a small part of me wondered if Sarah was perhaps a distraction from the reality of my empty existence; a life raft in a time of uncertainty to which I clung.

Dad rested his fork and knife across the plate. "No one's suggesting you move out. And like I've said before, we don't want you to get just any job. We think you should take your time and figure out what you want to pursue."

Their assurances gave me such a sense of liberation. My parents had always supported my interests—came to my ball games, driven me to piano lessons, sent me to Israel for a summer—so the last thing I wanted to do was disappoint them. Being with someone who was closer to retirement than they were, I feared, would do that. Which made keeping Sarah a secret the right choice.

That evening, I launched an ambitious organizing assault on myself. Upstairs, in my bedroom, fueled by the Sarah situation, I tackled batches of my life's stuff I hadn't been ready to part with the week before: college sweatshirts, high school trophies, board games. Each discarded item moved me one step further from my past and one step closer to my future.

"Feeling better?" Dad walked in, loosening his tie.

"A little. I know it's time to grow up, but I'm not sure what I'm supposed to do." I tossed a poster of Michael Jackson into my Boston Celtics garbage can.

"Think of this transition time as though it were another course. Call it Adulthood 101, but now it's up to you to write the syllabus, the steps to get you where you want to be. What is it you see yourself doing Monday morning?"

What did I see myself doing Monday morning? Sarah.

"I'd love to write a syndicated column. Sarah says not to worry and let time take its course."

"Sarah's a smart woman." Dad picked up an oversized maroon UMass sweatshirt from the Jackie pile, removed his glasses, put on the sweatshirt, then put his glasses back on. The sweatshirt fit his trim body and looked great against his white hair. "I had an idea. I've got this complicated filing project, and you're the perfect person for organizing it. What would you think of working in my office a few days a week?"

I didn't have to think. Having a reason to get up in the morning sounded good to me.

Nana T. hugged me as Papa and Uncle Mark placed a large cooler on the kitchen table. They'd arrived for Rosh Hashanah, and Cape Cod didn't sell the kosher foods they ate.

"Any traffic?" Dad always asked visitors this, his way of reminding himself of the blessing of where he lived.

"Not bad once we got out of the city," Mark said.

After hugging Meredith, Papa turned to me. It still shocked me to realize I was now taller than he was. I pictured him behind the deli counter in his Brooklyn grocery, slicing pastrami. I'd been eight when I had started working in his store on visits. He'd trusted me to ring up purchases on his old-fashioned cash register and to calculate exact change on my own. I remembered the time a customer wearing a leather jacket like the Fonz from *Happy Days* had said, "Murray, who's the little girl?" Papa had beamed, saying it was his granddaughter. "She's beautiful," the Fonz impersonator had replied. "Looks nothing like you." All the customers had laughed, even Papa. But as pleased as Papa had appeared, sadness had remained in his eyes. Only in the last year, as he'd begun sharing his experiences in the many concentration and labor camps he'd been in during the Holocaust, had I begun to understand where that sadness came from. It amazed me how he'd gone on with his life after his entire family had been collected like cattle, assigned a number, and then shot, gassed, or starved to death.

"How's by you, sweetheart?" Papa asked me in his Polish accent. "Got a job yet?"

"Give her five minutes to look," Mark answered for me.

"Okay, never mind. Come with me." Papa walked out the front door, hands clasped behind his back, a natural leader of a tribe.

Alone in the driveway, Papa stuffed five twenty-dollar bills into my palm. "Put this someplace you shouldn't lose it. Enjoy your life, sweetheart."

"Thanks, Papa." I stuffed the money into my pocket.

Before we went back in, I checked the mailbox. Seeing Sarah's handwriting on an envelope brought on the kind of smile that made people wonder what you're up to. I slipped her letter into my pocket along with the cash. Two secrets safe together.

> September 13, 1993
>
> Dear Felice,
>
> Seems a fine and beautiful monster has been created. I know this because it's not even a toss-up on winning the lottery or seeing you at the door. Any thoughts on turning off instant-mind replay? S.

In my bedroom, I entered the larger of my two closets. One side had a wall of cubbyholes filled with neatly folded stacks of polo shirts, jeans, and sweaters, along with trophies and shoes. Opposite the cubbies were double-hanging bars with shirts on the top, and pants and skirts below. I brushed aside some pants to find a cardboard box the size of a toaster. Inside the box were a dozen manila envelopes, each labeled with a different letter of the alphabet. When I came to "S" I slipped Sarah's note inside.

"I only have a second," I said to Sarah when I called. "My relatives are here."

"Can you get away tomorrow? I looked at a map, and Milford is halfway between us."

"Maybe," I said as my door opened and my uncle walked in. "I'll call you later." I hung up and looked at Mark. "Remember I told you I had a crush on my ex-boss?"

"Uh-huh." He sat beside me on the bed.

"Turns out she has a crush on me too."

"Are you interested in being with her?"

"It doesn't matter. She has a girlfriend. Plus, she's fifty-seven. People would say it was wrong."

"Who cares what people say? And who says it needs to be a relationship? I'm sure she can teach you a few things." He wagged his eyebrows up and down Groucho Marx style.

"Mark." I punched him.

"Look, you've been questioning your sexuality for a while, not to mention you're unsure about what to do with your life, so maybe having an affair with an older woman could help clarify a few things. Sarah could be your Mrs. Robinson, like in *The Graduate*."

"I don't seem to remember Mrs. Robinson being that great for Benjamin Braddock."

"She was a kind of wake-up call for him. When are you seeing her again?"

"Sarah wants to meet tomorrow. I know you guys just got here, and I feel guilty even considering it."

"Don't worry." He got up and walked over to my closet. "Let's pick out what you'll wear."

"Wear? I didn't know you were that kind of gay."

Sarah wore a navy sweater and jeans, with gold cat studs in her ears, a relaxed version of her I'd never seen. We were sitting in her car in the parking lot of a Burger King just off the highway. The moment I'd gotten into her car, she'd asked for a kiss. I'd wanted to, but when an overweight man came out of the fast-food joint stuffing a french fry into his mouth, I had concerns about someone seeing us. Sarah assured me no one cared about us in Milford but agreed to find another spot.

Under an overcast sky, we drove until we found a cemetery. Sarah parked beneath a tree whose spidery branches seemed to point at us accusingly. Unease spread through me at the thought of hanging around dead people's spirits, but Sarah said she loved the history and the seclusion. She leaned over the emergency brake and kissed me as raindrops pinged against the roof. It was romantic, the two of us in that sheltered spot, one shared intention. I had enjoyed kissing Kimberly, but this was different. Kissing Sarah sent shocks to the center of my belly. Got my juices flowing. Was it more intense because I had dreamed of this? Because I'd been in awe of her for so long? Or was it the high-stakes secrecy that intensified my want for more?

After an hour of making out, pausing occasionally to shake out a limb gone numb, Sarah fell back in her seat to catch her breath. The windows had fogged up. Sarah took my hand, sandwiched it in between hers. "I know I'm only a blip in your life, but the feelings I have for you are stronger than I've ever had for anyone."

"Even Linda?"

Sarah nodded. "I've never cheated on Linda. Never even considered it, but I find myself falling in love with you."

In love? With me?

Sarah had told me that when it came to love you either knew or you didn't. Did I love her back? I thought of her constantly but wasn't sure how to tell the difference between love and infatuation. A sociology professor had once said that the one who cares least in a relationship controls it. That's how I'd always handled relationships. No reason to stray from my M.O. now, especially with someone who could crush my heart in an instant. Tears stung the back of my eyes, catching me off guard. What was happening to me?

"I have a joke." I reverted to my other M.O. "Welcome to the reading of Manual Hirsch's will. To my two children I leave them each one million dollars. To my darling wife, I leave two million dollars and everything not in her name already. And last, but not least, to my brother-in-law, Louie, who never worked a day in his life. And who always told me I'd never remember him in my will." I paused. "Hello, Louie!"

Laughing, Sarah took my face in her hands. "I want to hold you. I could stay up all night just holding you. When you stay over next week, I'm not sure I'll be able to hold back."

"I don't want you to hold back, but I'm nervous because I'm not sure what I did with Kimberly classifies me as experienced." For the first time I wasn't intimidated to admit the thoughts I was having about sex with someone I was…dating? Was that what we were doing? I was sure Sarah had done every sexual thing imaginable, while I was brand-spanking new to lesbian sex. Or straight sex for that matter.

"Don't worry." Sarah released my cheeks. "We won't do anything you don't want to do."

"But that's the point. I want to do everything with you. Even stuff I don't know I want to do." Just then another of Sarah's adages popped into my head: "Whatever you don't know, I know. Whatever I don't know, you know. And whatever we both don't know isn't worth knowing." What did we know then? What did we pretend wasn't worth knowing? Had we thought through the consequences of our actions instead of acting on our wants, we might've predicted the ending of our affair and avoided it altogether. But we were falling in love, certain only good would come of it.

"How are you feeling about us?" Sarah asked.

"Part of me thinks I should just enjoy this and not worry, since there's no way this will go anywhere, because you're with Linda. But I can't stop thinking about you."

"I can't stop thinking about you either. I'm sorry it's hard for you. Just know that whatever happens." Sarah placed her hand on my chest above my left breast. "I'm still there in your heart."

We drove back to Burger King holding hands. Before I got out, Sarah handed me a mixtape, telling me to listen to Ann Reed's song "If You Were Mine," saying that the lyrics summed up how she'd been feeling.

As I cruised home, Ann's rich voice sailed through my speakers: "We've been friends many years / and all that time / I have been wond'ring what it would be like / if you were mine."

A warmth settled over me. The thought of Sarah wanting me brought with it comfort and security, and filled me with a hunger I hadn't realized was there. I had always equated being in love with being vulnerable and had tried to avoid it. But now that I'd had a taste, I realized the only thing it made you was happy.

Watching my wipers smooth away fat splotches of rain, I thought of Mark's suggestion about Sarah being a learning experience and that I should keep my heart out of it. It might've been too late.

My grandparents hugged me the moment I walked into the house as though I'd been away a year and not just the afternoon. My guilt at leaving to see Sarah spiked through the roof.

"Your mom asked me where you were," Mark whispered as we entered the dining room. "She's worried about you."

Before I could respond, Papa clapped his hand onto my back. "There's a man I want you should meet. He's twenty-six, works in the jewelry district, and will make you happy."

"Thanks, but I'm not in the market for a husband right now."

"Are you ever going to get married?" Meredith sat down across from me with attentive eyes.

"I'm waiting for the perfect man." I made a mental note to thank Sarah for the diplomatic line.

"Well, it doesn't seem like you're working on it," she said.

"How can you be sure I'm not seeing anyone now?" I caught my parents look at each other, alert.

"Felice." Meredith tilted her head, the grown-up mannerism adorable set against her pigtails. "If you had a boyfriend, we'd know."

Nice double life I led.

"How's it going?" Gina walked into the file room where I was seated amid stacks of cardboard boxes filled with legal cases representing failed businesses. For years, Dad had been saying that one wrong decision could destroy your prospects for happiness. No wonder I was fearful when it came to making them.

"You mean, 'How's it going closing bankruptcy petitions and driving my sister to after-school activities?'" The truth was, working at my dad's office gave me structure. I needed structure. Was lost without it.

"It's temporary. You're just getting your footing." Gina hiked up her ankle-length paisley skirt and sat down on a box.

"Yeah? Tell that to my foot." I wrote "closed" in black marker across a hulking file folder and dropped it onto a stack of others.

"Dating anyone?" Gina had been a paralegal at my dad's law firm for a decade. We'd become friends when I'd come to the office to type my high school papers on the computer.

"They don't live on the Cape."

"They?" Gina was good. She was married, no kids, and acted in local theater productions. I judged her to be open-minded.

I reached for another file and glanced at the door. "You won't tell my dad?"

"Ooh, juicy already." She clapped her hands. "I swear."

"I'm kind of dating an older woman."

"What do you mean kind of? And how old? Forty?" Gina was forty.

I shook my head. "Fifty-seven. And she lives with someone."

Gina smirked. "You're not living a boring life, my friend. You're living a soap opera."

"You're not shocked about me seeing an older woman?"

"What's age got to do with love?"

"Yeah, what's love got to do with it?" Dad crooned as he walked into the room. My heart raced. I looked at Gina, feeling afraid. She shook her head to assure me he hadn't heard. "I'm going to Orleans to see a client," he said. "Want to come? You can talk about what love is with me." Did he know? Was that why he'd asked me to tag along? Did he plan on saying something? But he didn't. He never said a word.

Early the next morning I went for a bike ride and stopped at Craigville Beach, climbed the lifeguard tower, and stared at the ocean. The waves were still, the surface almost pond-like. Fat seagulls dove into the water, snatching crabs as locals walked the shoreline past enormous summer homes, their windows boarded up for the off-season. I breathed in the salty air and opened my journal. As my pen moved across the page, recalling each detail of my night with Sarah, I grinned. Until I wrote: "We can't tell anyone." Panic set in, which was strange since I had felt the same way about my relationship with Kimberly, but it had never elicited such angst. Why this time? Was it because missing Sarah felt physical? Because I couldn't stop thinking of her? Because, for the first time, I wanted to tell people? My emotions had never felt this out of control. Was this how you gauged love? I had no clue. All I knew was I wanted to be with Sarah any chance I could get.

"Alumni office," answered the receptionist.

"I'm sorry, I was trying to reach admissions. Is it possible for you to transfer me?" I gave Sarah's direct line. Seconds later I heard, "Sarah," her voice firm and efficient.

"It's me," I whispered.

"Can you hold a second?" Sarah's businesslike tone sounded as though she didn't want to talk. Had something happened? Bile crept up into my throat. We'd only spoken twice since we'd met in Milford the week before. Sarah feared calling my house in case my parents answered, and I was reluctant to rack up charges on my parents' phone bill.

"I'm sorry." Sarah's voice was back to the softer one I was now privy to. The admissions director had been in her office and she'd made up an excuse to end their meeting early. "Are you in Amherst? The call came from on campus."

"No. But on my bike ride this morning I had the idea to call the alumni 800 number and have them transfer me. Now I can call, and it won't show on my parents' phone bill."

"You're a genius," Sarah said.

"But I'm hesitant to call in case you have people in your office."

"Call at four. Most everyone has left by then. It's the hardest hour of the day, watching the approaching sunset and not sharing it with you. Now I'll have something to look forward to until you're back. Five days and counting."

"I know! I can't wait to get a popover from Judie's and a Bruegger's honey-grain bagel and—"

"Is it only the food you miss?" Sarah asked.

"What are you, nuts?"

Seated on a bench several yards from where Emily had secluded herself inside the Dickinson homestead, I waited for Sarah. It was late-September and the trees were giving off mini bursts of orange, yellow, and red fireworks. Leaf-peeping season had begun.

When Sarah pulled up in her car, she was wearing orange-tinted sunglasses, her arm resting out the window, her gold watch glittering in the sun. I got in the car and Sarah took my hand. She drove down Main Street, turned up the steep incline of Triangle Street and at the top, pulled into West Cemetery, a historic burying ground fenced off behind a row of downtown commercial buildings. Many of the names on the crumbling tombstones dotting the sloping knolls had worn away or been overgrown with moss and were no longer decipherable.

We walked over to three gravestones enclosed by a wrought-iron fence. "Called back" was all it said under Emily Dickinson's name.

"I died for beauty, but was scarce / Adjusted in the tomb," Sarah quoted before nudging me.

"When one who died for truth was lain / In an adjoining room," I added. Back and forth, line by line, we recited the first poem she'd ever had me memorize.

I picked up two tiny rocks, then handed one to Sarah. "Did you know it's a Jewish tradition to leave rocks on a headstone to show you've visited?"

"See how much I'm learning from you?" Sarah placed her rock beside mine on Emily's headstone. As we walked back to the car, Sarah placed her hand on my lower back, her touch making me feel safe. "Autumn days are like gifts. Today would've been perfect for a trip to Stockbridge or anywhere, as long as it's us together."

"Let's go to Tanglewood now." I pictured us heading west on the Mass Pike to see James Taylor.

"Tempting. You're like my BluBlocker sunglasses. You block out all my rational thinking and only let me see the possibilities." Sarah was fanatical about her sunglasses, keeping multiple pairs in her car. She was also prepared for weather surprises. In her trunk, she had a bag of kitty litter in case her car got stuck in snow, and peanut-butter crackers in case, while stuck, she got hungry. Sarah lived every facet of her life with caution. Except one.

"Thank you, Sarah."

"For what, Blu?" Already the nickname worked.

"For taking a chance and hiring me as the night director last summer. And for this. Us." I gestured between us. "My life is so uncertain, but when I'm with you, I get this sense that everything will work out. Does that sound crazy?"

"Not at all." Sarah took my hand. Then we made out in her car until she had to get back to work.

That evening Jackie and I went to Yom Kippur services run by the UMass Hillel group, an annual event I'd attended with Rachel since my freshman year. It was nice to share this ritual with my sister.

Inside the Student Union Ballroom, we sat among undergraduates, administrators, and locals facing a makeshift stage with the rabbi and Torah on it. But the real spiritual and dramatic view was behind it. Outside the windows, reflected off the Morrill Science Center's windows, was an intense purple-and-pink sunset creating a wondrous, calming glow.

"It's a sign from God." The rabbi nodded to the sight behind him. "A gesture He is here to help us through this solemn day of reflection." The rabbi went on to speak of the annual atonement of Jews on Yom Kippur, and about honesty and new beginnings.

The breakup with Kimberly, I reasoned, was the honest thing to do. The situation with Sarah was my new beginning. And though being with her was a learning experience, I couldn't avoid that it could end up as something to atone for. To be on the safe side, I figured I should ask someone with a little more authority on the subject.

"God," I said in my head, figuring He might be in earshot for the High Holiday, "if what I'm doing is bad, why am I so happy?"

No response. Yom Kippur was God's busiest day of the year.

After services I floored it to Sarah's, hopefulness racing through me, a sensation I hadn't had in months. With all my windows open, the crisp earthy aroma of farms and woods wafted in as Ann Reed's voice sailed out at full volume. The inky sky highlighted the almost-full moon, while black outlines of the Mount Holyoke Range looked like jagged teeth coming up for a bite.

Speeding up The Notch, the steep mountain route separating Amherst from Holyoke, I passed a Pioneer Valley Transit Authority bus filled with female students heading back to Mount Holyoke College. I envied their lives as students; whereas my title was about to become the other woman. We'd only kissed, a lesser transgression than what I knew was coming, yet I felt disconnected from what was happening, as though I were watching actors in a movie. Would they or wouldn't they sleep together? Absurd question. Sure they would. What's more? I wanted them to.

In Sarah's driveway, I parked behind Linda's car. She was out of town, and I was there to replace her, if only until she returned. Walking up to the house, overnight bag in hand, I told myself this wasn't cheating, not technically, since Sarah and Linda weren't legally married. I knew that reasoning was wrong—cheating is cheating—but Sarah was the one being unfaithful, not me. I told myself that had Sarah not revealed her feelings, this wouldn't be happening as I would never have acted on my attraction to her otherwise. I trusted Sarah knew what she was doing, that she wouldn't let anything happen to me, and that it would be okay. Which is why, on that magical autumn night, I let the anticipation of making love to Sarah trump doing the right thing.

Standing on the front steps, I glimpsed Sarah through the living room window, reading the newspaper, cat on her lap. Despite my aversion to cats, I had to admit she looked at peace. I wanted to laugh. The rabbi had just said that peace was what you'd have the more your life was without sin. And if I sinned on the first day of the new year, was it all downhill? Casting that thought away, I balled up my fist and knocked.

"Hello, Louie!" Sarah repeated the punch line from the joke I'd told her in Milford when she opened the door. We shared a lingering kiss in the foyer before Sarah led me in a slow dance. Jazz music played as we moved, our cheeks and bodies pressed together. I pictured romantic movies I'd seen. Never had I seen our version.

"How about we get ready for bed," Sarah said. No question where I'd be sleeping that evening. I stripped down to a T-shirt and panties. Slipping under the covers, my nerves felt on edge. I wasn't scared it would hurt as it had with Josh, but I felt anxious I might feel as empty as when I'd had sex with Kimberly.

"Sorry, boys. Mama's got other plans tonight." Sarah lifted Maxi and Cody off the bed and carried them into the living room. Returning, she closed the French doors and lit two candles. The aroma of vanilla filled the air. I lay as still as a photograph, watching shadows of the flickering candlelight dance on the wall. Was I about to make love with someone who'd been having sex longer than I'd been alive?

Sarah stood beside the bed wearing reading glasses, and opened a book. "'That I did always love— / I bring thee proof—/ That till I loved— / I never lived—Enough—' Our pal Emily Dickinson."

"Poetry and candles? Who knew you were such a romantic?"

"Let's keep that between us." Sarah lay beside me, staring into my eyes, as she traced her fingers over my breasts. My nipples hardened. She lifted my T-shirt over my head. The cool air made me shiver, so she covered me with the bed sheet and continued to caress my skin gently, each part coming alive under her touch. I pulled Sarah closer. Years of fooling around had left me unsatisfied and ravenous.

"Whoa," she said. "We're not in a rush. The night is long." Had Kimberly or Josh said that I would've been embarrassed, but Sarah was my mentor, and I was there to learn.

Sarah disappeared under the sheet. She slid off my underwear, inching it down, as if savoring every moment of opening a present. I reached to hurry the process, and she brushed my hand away, saying, "My job." She soon reappeared with my panties dangling from her finger. "You *are* turned on." Again, had it been anyone else who said that? Mortification.

Sarah straddled my hips and kissed each breast tenderly, before working her way down, kissing every part of my skin. When she passed my belly button my body stiffened.

"Relax," she said.

Not like I wasn't trying.

Opening me up, her tongue stroked with a tempered cadence. I tried to relax. I tried to breathe. I tried to focus as she buried her face in the space between. Josh and Kimberly had never done that. And it wasn't something I'd ever done to them. I willed myself not to giggle, as the sensation tickled. Soon a buildup of heat and pleasure followed. I gripped the sheets. Part of me wanted her to stop as it grew intense, but I was curious where it was going. Like water breaching the top of a dam, the pressure turned into this total release of my muscles and thoughts. My entire body shuddered.

Seconds later, the full length of Sarah's naked body was on top of mine, our parts lining up, sealing us together. She began to rub against me. We created friction, like two sticks starting a fire. Droplets of sweat pooled between us. As that same sensual buildup grew inside me, Sarah let out her own tiny, guttural moans and we came together.

She slipped off and gently turned me onto my side, my back to her. Wrapping her arm around me, Sarah held me close, her bent knees inside the pockets of my bent knees. I marked that moment as the time I lost my virginity. Anyone could have sex, but to experience the passion supporting it: that's when it should count.

"I love you," Sarah whispered. The words "I love you too" reached my tongue, but remained there unspoken.

~

I woke, my head rising and falling on Sarah's chest, her breathing rhythmic. I snatched my glasses from the headboard shelf and looked beyond the two cats curled at our feet. The cable box read 7:12. Outside, leaves just beginning to turn color swayed. The bedroom doors were open, the candles snuffed out. Sarah must've done that after I'd fallen asleep. I replaced my glasses on the shelf, and the movement woke Sarah. She hoisted my body onto hers and guided my hips in gradual movements. As that same tingling sensation grew, I held my breath to slow the release.

"Breathe," Sarah insisted.

"But I want to make sure it's working for you too."

"Trust me. It works for me big time."

I continued to gyrate against her. With her eyes closed, she murmured, "Yes, yes," in low throaty breaths, so I moved faster, attuned to following her directions. I stared at her, a bit in shock. I'd been in awe of her for so long and now we were making love. Not to mention she was *in* love with me. Was I in love with her? My body certainly was.

Sarah's breathing grew more intense, as did my personal interrogation. What would people think if they found out I was with an older woman? Would they think something was wrong with me? Would they feel the same if I was with an older man? Not ready for the answers, I closed my eyes, shut off my brain, and welcomed that now familiar sensation coursing through my body as Sarah let out her own long whimper.

I collapsed, breathless, my cheek on her chest, the sound of her heart thumping into my ear. "Do I please you?" I whispered.

"Blu." Sarah wrapped her arms around me. "You please me just by smiling that thousand-watt smile."

In seconds I fell back to sleep.

When I opened my eyes, Sarah was leaning on her elbow, chin in her hand, studying me. "I don't want to let go of this moment. I'm amazed how tender I am with you. I don't want to hurt you, as though you're so fragile."

I drummed my knuckles against my head, derailing the seriousness of the discussion. "See? Not so fragile."

She smiled. "How about pancakes?"

"It's Yom Kippur, remember? I'm fasting." I might not have had a legitimate motive to atone the night before, but this morning was a different story. Sarah offered to fast with me, claiming there were a few things she could atone for, and asked if there were other holiday rituals. I explained that on Rosh Hashanah our family walked to the beach and threw stones into the ocean, imagining they were our sins, allowing us to start the year with a clean slate. After last night I'd need an entire bag of stones.

In the shower, Sarah wrapped her hands around me from behind, as she'd done the first time we'd played golf, only now her fingers slid into crevices not exposed on golf courses.

While toweling off, my feet nestled in the fluffy bathroom mat, I caught sight of our reflection in the full-length mirror. Comparing our bodies—the looseness of her skin, the firmness of my own—made me again question the appropriateness of our coupling. Her body didn't turn me off or on, as I'd never been attracted to body parts, with men or women. What drew me to Sarah was her intelligence, cleverness, and sophistication, and how she looked at me—as though the simple act of seeing me brought her joy.

"You've got an incredible body." Sarah ran her fingers between my thighs. I shut my eyes. In my mind what we were doing felt right. Seeing it reflected in the mirror might've made me question that.

An hour later, we were stealing kisses on the golf cart at Cherry Hill, each move a calculated chance to not get caught.

Back in Sarah's car I tallied the scorecard. "I beat you by two."

"No surprise. You're a natural."

"Well, I had a great teacher." I took Sarah's hand as she pulled out of the dusty parking lot. "But I'm sure there's still more to learn."

Twenty minutes later, Sarah parked behind the Montague Bookmill, a sprawling red building that had once been a gristmill but was now a used bookstore and coffeehouse.

We stood on the back porch above the fast-moving Sawmill

River. Trees along the water were just beginning to show hints of color. Sarah removed two stones from her pocket and handed me one. "I know this isn't the holiday you do this," Sarah said, "but didn't think it could hurt."

Would throwing a rock into the water absolve me from sleeping with Sarah, a "married" woman? Instead of dwelling on the obvious answer, I cocked my arm back and hurled the stone.

We entered the Bookmill through the second floor. It had a musty odor, like Sarah's closet. I followed Sarah through compact rooms with bowed hardwood floors and shelves upon shelves of worn books about history, religion, and travel. People of all ages were skimming through books or sitting in worn-out upholstered chairs, reading in shafts of sunlight.

At the top of a staircase, Sarah spun around so abruptly I almost bumped into her. "No matter what happens," she said, her expression serious. "We'll always have the Bookmill." Then she gave me a quick kiss, turned and descended the curving staircase, me close behind.

Downstairs was an enormous room with a high ceiling, more shelves of books, and a sign with the store's motto: "Books you don't need in a place you can't find."

We separated to browse. After we met back up, Sarah insisted on paying for the two books I found: *The Alchemist* by Paulo Coelho, and a lesbian mystery by Rita Mae Brown in which the sleuth's partner was a cat. Sarah herself had a paperback of poetry.

We entered the adjacent café. The aroma of cinnamon and coffee permeated the air. Not an ideal place to be when fasting, but smelling was allowed. Locals in flannel shirts sat at small tables, gabbing over steaming mugs. We sat near two elderly men playing chess.

Under the table, Sarah found my foot with hers. "It's been said that one of golf's attractions, despite the frustrations and momentary flashes of brilliance, is that when you play, you're unaware of anything else. True or false?"

"True." I was aware of her obsession.

"False. The other day during my match my head was not in the game. Can you guess what was playing in my cranial VCR?"

"Me?"

"Bingo." Sarah held up her book, *The Dream of a Common Language* by Adrienne Rich. "Want to see her when you come back for Homecoming?"

I nodded.

"And what about dinner beforehand? Care to join us for that too?"

I stopped nodding.

"Not the ideal situation, I know, but Linda and I already have plans to go, and I want you to hear Adrienne."

"Okay." I knew this was what I'd signed up for: a clandestine relationship that would take a back burner to her legitimate one.

Sarah opened her book and began to read. I opened one of my books but all I could think about was what she'd said the morning after our first night together. "If you meet someone next week, don't let me keep you from falling in love." But how was I to meet someone else with my mind and heart engrossed in her?

"She came at that precise junction in a life, when the past is unbearable, and the future uncertain," I said, quoting the Rita Mae Brown poem Sarah had made me learn. Sarah looked up at me. "Which one of us was she?" I asked. "You or me?"

That evening I picked up Jackie, and we met Sarah and Rachel at the Iron Horse Music Hall in Northampton. Leah Kunkel, slated to sing a duet with Livingston Taylor, was a friend of Sarah's, so we got to meet them both before the concert. Livingston was a doppelganger of his older brother, James.

We sat at a table near the stage, Sarah's thigh pressed against mine. Giddiness tickled my insides until I caught Rachel staring at us. Her expression was perplexed, confirming my fear that if people knew about me and Sarah, they would look at us with that same befuddlement—before that gaze then dissolved into disapproval.

After the concert I drove Jackie back to her dorm and flew to Sarah's house. No candles this time, but plenty of heat.

Early the next morning I went for a run. It drizzled, but I barely noticed, so lost in thought was I about Sarah liking me, as though I'd won some coveted award. Being the center of her attention gave me that same high as running, endorphins flooding my system. But as great as I felt, I was aware the relationship could disappear at any moment—say if Linda found out or if Sarah's conscience returned and she simply ended it—and that thought filled me with dread. Without Sarah, I feared that hole she filled within me, the one I hadn't even known existed, would open again and I would sink.

At noon we headed to the Pleasant Street Theater in Northampton to see *The Age of Innocence,* a film based on the Edith Wharton novel. Sarah insisted on paying for my ticket, saying, "I make more money than you. When the day comes you make more, you can pay." Fair enough. We held hands in the tiny basement theater, shocked by how much the film's plot—the struggle with choosing between one's yearnings and one's duty to family—resembled our situation.

On the drive back we stopped at a deli near Sarah's house, and she bought the Sunday *New York Times.* We read the paper seated on the couch, my feet in her lap, classical music playing on the stereo, cats curled up in places. I felt like an imposter. Technically I looked like an adult, but there was still so much to learn.

When the phone rang Sarah spoke to the caller before handing it to me. "Your sister."

"Kimberly called looking for you," Jackie said.

"Did you tell her I was here? Not that it's a big deal, but—"

"I didn't," Jackie said.

"Good, thanks." I hung up and called Kimberly. We hadn't spoken since we'd broken up two weeks before.

"Can you explain what you weren't getting from me?" Kimberly's voice resonated anger.

"I told you. It wasn't you. I'm going through a lot." I repeated myself on purpose. "Repetition is knowledge," Sarah always said. After twenty minutes of talking in circles, Kimberly hung up on me. I knew she was struggling but I knew breaking up with her had been the right move for both of us. How I felt with Sarah made me realize what I had had with Kimberly, while special, was not true love. But was it true love with Sarah? My heart was leaning toward yes, but my mind, as usual, was holding me back.

~

"What's up with you and Sarah?" Rachel asked the moment we sat down at a table inside Judie's. The popular Amherst restaurant was buzzing for a Monday. Locals and businesspeople, nibbling sizable popovers, filled the sunny space.

"What do you mean?" Even though the memory of Sarah lingered on my lips, I lied right through them.

"Don't act so innocent." Rachel squeezed a wedge of lemon into her iced tea. "I suspected something by how you two were acting the other night at the Iron Horse."

"How were we acting?"

"Flirting. And the way Sarah looked at you. Or couldn't stop looking at you." Rachel dropped the lemon into her glass. "So, this morning I asked her, and she didn't deny it. I was half expecting and half hoping she would."

Wait a minute—Sarah told Rachel?

"If this gets out, Felice, can you imagine the scandal?"

"We're not planning on taking out an ad in the *Collegian*."

"Not funny. You're treading in dangerous waters."

Our waiter placed two large popovers on our table. I split mine apart and watched steam rise from the eggy center.

"Look." I dipped a piece of popover into the apple butter and ate it, not caring that it burned my tongue. "My life's crazy right now. All my friends are moving forward with their lives, while I'm living at home without direction. Sarah's the only thing that makes me happy."

"That doesn't mean you can waltz in and be with someone who's already in a relationship." Rachel ripped open her own popover, but left it cooling on the plate. "Sarah's dance card might have been full back in her day, but now she's with Linda."

Her dance card? Jesus, how old was she?

"Have you considered how Linda would feel if she found out?" Was Rachel kidding? That was the one thing I tried not to think about. And the more I tried not to, the more I thought about it, which only added to my mounting pile of guilt. Linda had no clue that her world had become a lie, that the woman she shared a home with was in love with me. When I felt this remorse, I reminded myself that if Linda didn't find out she wouldn't get hurt. Illogical, but I was grasping at straws.

"Why is age more than a number when it comes to love?" I quoted Prince, Rachel's favorite singer.

Rachel wagged her knife at me before dipping it into the apple butter. "Keep in mind that the age disparity isn't your biggest problem here."

No kidding.

After that oh-so-fun lunch with Rachel, I found Sarah in her car waiting for me outside admissions.

"Why didn't you tell me you were going to tell Rachel about us?" I said, getting in. "She just gave me an earful about how what we're doing is so wrong."

"I wasn't planning to, but it was good to talk." Sarah tossed the *Times Book Review* she'd been reading into the backseat. "God knows I've listened to Rachel discuss her personal issues over the years."

But these weren't only Sarah's issues; they were mine too.

"Aren't you concerned she might tell Linda?"

"Let's not worry about that." Sarah squeezed my knee. "There's a place I want to show you."

We drove north on Route 116, zooming passed Bub's BBQ, a restaurant I'd frequented with my *Collegian* friends after intramural softball games; Goten, the Japanese restaurant Josh had taken me to, where servers stir-fried vegetables and meat at your table; and Sugarloaf Frosty, the soft ice cream shop Kimberly and I had frequented often. I was on turbo speed, rushing through my past in a hurry to arrive—still hopeful—at my future.

A half hour later Sarah turned onto a one-lane dirt road, daylight shaded by trees the farther we drove into the thickening woods. About a mile in, Sarah cut the engine. "Welcome to Rattlesnake Gutter."

Dried twigs crunched beneath our feet as we walked beside a stream, birds chirping in surround sound. Sarah stopped at a boulder, leaned back against its flat surface and drew me to her, kissing me passionately.

When we parted, I pulled from my pocket a handmade card I'd

made of two cats kissing with the caption "You're purrfect." For a non-fan of felines, I wasn't half bad at drawing them.

"What am I to do with this?" Sarah replied.

Not the response I was expecting.

"I didn't give it to you to post on your refrigerator." I snapped. Sarah was no longer my boss; I was no longer intimidated.

"I'm sorry, Blu. This means so much, it's just the circumstances."

Ah yes, the circumstances—the motto of our affair, the go-to excuse whenever Sarah couldn't be with me because of previous commitments with Linda. The circumstances were straightforward: Sarah had a partner, Sarah didn't want to hurt her partner, and we were too far apart in age to make being together fair to me. I accepted it. Accepted all of it as though this was how relationships worked. It would take decades and several repeated affairs for me to see that this was, in fact, the opposite of how healthy relationships functioned.

Sarah removed a Swiss Army knife from her pocket and carved our initials into a birch tree. I carved a heart around our initials and added the date. Sarah took a picture with her camera, and then we left, driving in reverse down the narrow dirt road.

"Are you okay?" I asked Sarah that evening. She was lying in bed, propped up by pillows, open book resting on her chest, staring into space.

"I'm scared."

"Of what?" I assumed nothing scared Sarah.

"In all my relationships, never have I fallen this deep, this fast." She blotted her watery eyes with a tissue.

"Since it's forbidden, that could be what makes it more intense."

She forced a smile. "When did you become so wise, Blu?"

Despite our limited time together, the warmth between us was only increasing. With Linda returning the next day, we didn't know when the next opportunity to be together would present itself. I would be back in a month for Homecoming, but seeing Sarah would be difficult, and spending the night together impossible.

Sarah asked, "Do you remember when I said, 'If you fall in love with someone don't let this get in your way?'"

I nodded.

"At least wait a few weeks." She moved aside her book and guided my head to rest on her chest. I felt the rhythm of her heartbeat. Surrounded by the cats and the memory of what we'd done and the expectation of what we had yet to do, my tears fell quietly.

"Say cheese," Sarah whispered the next morning. I opened one eye. She was standing beside the bed, her camera focused on me.

"Why are you taking my picture?" We'd slept little, not wanting to waste one minute of our last night together.

"I don't want to forget this moment."

"Why are you wearing soft clothes?"

"I'm blowing off work. We've got to de-Felice the house. Your curly hair is worse than the cat hair."

"Nothing's worse than cat hair."

Ignoring my dig, Sarah held out a glass filled with a pink liquid. "They say grapefruit juice staves off cancer."

"Who's they?" I downed the juice and went into the bathroom to brush my teeth. Every summer Sarah told the counselors, "If you're tired, brushing your teeth will wake you up." Now more awake, I walked into the kitchen and saw Sarah sliding the few cards I'd given her into her briefcase.

"They'll be safer at the office," she said, meaning safe from Linda finding them. As ecstatic as I was, I was reminded that our happiness was an illusion that could burst at any moment, reality a misstep away. A letter falling into the wrong hands, a long curly hair under the covers. Ours was a love based on fear, and fear douses the body with endorphins, giving off a natural high, which explained why I was jonesing for more. After avoiding alcohol and drugs my whole life, I'd become an addict anyway.

We spent the morning stripping bedsheets, washing dishes, and bagging garbage, moving as if in a time-lapse movie montage, a Kenny Loggins's soundtrack playing in the background. Our time together had been so dreamlike, but now, as we stood on the back porch shaking strands of my hair loose from the comforter, it occurred to me how far we'd transgressed.

September 29, 1993

Dear Blu,

It's been 24 hours since you left. Already I'm flashing on images of our long weekend: soft, tender partings, layers of intimacy beyond the rain and wet and general sogginess, dinners awash with smiling eyes, hands that can't stop touching, profiles in the flickering light, sweet closeness, night skin, soft skin, silky essence, rising love tension, rapid, surging passion, sweet cries of pleasure, soft kisses of ultimate intimacy. Cuddling and closeness. Deep sleep. Morning stirring and tender touching. Another day for stolen hours, another day to celebrate our love. Even though you're gone, those lessons have left their imprint. I'm still there. S.

October 2, 1993

Dear Sarah,

I now understand what you meant when you said, "You'll know when it happens to you." Roads and rivers and years may separate us, but it doesn't matter to me. Does it to you? I have experienced little, so how perfect then to have someone teach me the wonders of life. I will add it to the multitude of lessons I've already learned from you. ♥Blu

October 4, 1993

Dear Blu,

Today the trees are so beautiful and are creeping into my shaky picture of reality and along the ends is the crazy sense we should be together sharing this glorious valley autumn. I cheered myself up with retail therapy. Bought five turtlenecks (brings the total to 27!). I can hear you telling me to get rid of five old ones. Will try. I'm sitting through endless meetings, but would rather dream of our days, my last conscious image, you in my arms. Hope you are making progress on your room. Picture you like old-time movies organizing your stuff. I can see your brain spinning with what's next and being frustrated with living and planning one day at a time, right? To be continued. S.

October 6, 1993

Dear Sarah,

Writing to you is almost as good as being with you. Same with reading your letters. I lose myself in your words. I love knowing your letters are hidden in my closet to be reread anytime. I don't tell you often enough how much I appreciate you being there. Not "there" there, but "still there" as you say, in my heart. It warms me. It makes me smile. ♥Blu

October 9, 1993

Dear Blu,

Got my pictures back and enclosed the doubles. Your eyes have a different expression after certain "activities" have occurred. Made me want to kiss you awake like I couldn't do the first time you slept over. At Panda today this was my fortune: "You will have good luck in your personal affairs." Think it already came true. While there, flashed on an image of you sitting across the table that day looking at me with eyes I hoped no one else saw. You weren't even aware you were doing it, were you? How did we ever get from there to here? When was it every ounce of inhibition, control, and logical thinking flew out the window? Clearly my brain wasn't in charge. Kenny Loggins's song "Only a Miracle" hit me like a ton of Big Berthas. "And when I held you, I held a miracle in my hand." YOU are my miracle. I am waiting until 4:00 for your call. I haven't done any work since your letter came. Just reading and rereading, reliving it, remembering it and knowing it is truly a miracle. S.

October 11, 1993

Dear Sarah,

No, I won't burn your letters as you asked today; they're all I've got. Please don't burn mine. Maybe one day I'll write about us. I can always say it's fiction. Who would believe it? Okay, my eyes are getting heavy. How the hell did we stay up all night? Oh yeah, I remember. . . ♥Blu

October 13, 1993

Dear Blu,

My head is whirling, and it's an effort to keep the tears from surfacing. Have to get back to euphoria over our miracle. This "Great Pretender" shit is NOT GOOD. I'm so muddled I've fluctuated from extreme happiness to total hopelessness. I assumed it would be easy to compartmentalize my life, but it's not working. If asked how I felt, not sure I could hold it together. I am aware that this current, crazy fragile state of my head will pass, and I will be or appear to be the old me, but I won't ever be the same and I can smile about that because you are part of my heart. No matter what happens, I'll always be there. S.

P.S. Promise you won't write about me until after I'm dead. And make me taller.

October 16, 1993

Dear Sasquatch, (You asked to be taller)

Been thinking about our talk yesterday. Or rather, how you had to cut it short because you were meeting Linda and friends for dinner. I understand you have a life apart from me, but I don't have one apart from you, which is why I'm so excited to be heading back to Amherst on Thursday! ♥Blu

October 19, 1993

Dear Blu,

An excerpt from an Emily Dickinson poem I thought you'd like:

> If you were coming in the Fall,
> I'd brush the Summer by
> With half a smile and half a spurn,
> As Housewives do a Fly.
>
> If I could see you in a year,
> I'd wind the months in balls—
> And put them each in separate Drawers,
> Until their time befalls...
>
> If certain, when this life was out,
> That yours and mine should be,
> I'd toss it yonder like a rind,
> And taste eternity...

Another right-on gem by the Belle of Amherst, your friend and mine. I can see the image of "winding up the months in balls and sticking them in drawers." This should appeal to your closet cleaning soul. It occurs to me we're both hamstrung by living with our families, a situation I never dreamed would be a factor in curtailing and controlling my life. How we can't even predict the future. WOFTOG! S.

After getting Meredith onto the school bus, I took off for Western Mass like Cinderella headed to the ball. I arrived at Dynamite Records in Northampton, where Sarah had suggested we meet. "Discreet," she'd said. Only one other person was in the shop: a twenty-something guy with shoulder-length hair sitting behind the cash register, reading a comic book. I was rifling through a bin of used CDs, when a hand slipped around my waist.

"What are you doing?" I whispered, glancing at the cashier, whose head remained buried in his book. As good as Sarah's touch felt, my fear of someone seeing us trumped everything. Northampton might have recently been named "Lesbianville, U.S.A." by the *National Enquirer*, a sensationalist article that upset many folks at the time, but still, we couldn't stop being cautious.

"Sorry, Blu. It's been too long since I've seen you."

"It's only been four weeks."

"Four minutes is too long."

We walked up Main Street, our pinkies brushing, fulfilling that need to be touching every chance we got.

"It's nice I've regained my appetite." Sarah patted her noticeably flatter stomach after ordering us sandwiches from the Vermont Country Deli. "Would you believe I lost a whopping ten pounds in one month? The Felice Diet works wonders. No Felice, no appetite."

I wondered if Kimberly had lost weight too.

The sidewalks were full of people enjoying the warm autumn weather. I picked up a copy of the *Valley Advocate*, planning to write to the editor about freelance submissions, when someone called Sarah's name. We turned to see Nan, Sarah's friend from her dinner party, her head and shoulders blocking the sun. I'd forgotten how tall she was.

"You remember Felice," Sarah said.

Nan looked down at me with an I-know-you're-up-to-something glance. "Will you be joining us at the Rich reading tonight?"

"Yes, Felice will be there," Sarah said for me. "See you there."

We walked away. It took all my willpower not to turn around to see if Nan was watching us.

We took Sarah's car to (where else?) a cemetery in Florence. Bright-red maple leaves collected on the windshield.

"A little something for you." Sarah handed me a copy of the *Women's Traveler*, an annual guidebook of lesbian-friendly vacation spots. I opened the cover. "To Blu, In my dreams, I'm taking you away. I love you. Sarah."

My heart sank. I handed the book back. "I don't want it."

"Why not?"

"Because this is a book of dream vacations. We'll never go on one."

"Don't say that. I never dreamed I'd fall in love again. And I did."

"But what are we doing? At first it was exciting, but now hiding out in your car seems pathetic." Screw her no-whining rule. Why had my mood soured? Was it the reminder that we were a secret? But wasn't that how I preferred my relationships? I'd thought I was okay with the sneaking around, but suddenly I wanted more. How much more I didn't know. Even if Linda wasn't in the picture, there was still the issue of our age difference.

"I wish I could take your pain and confusion away," Sarah said. "Yes, there's an element that's hard, but our time is more precious than that of a couple who lives together." Couple—the one thing we'd never be. Was that what had me upset? Being the other woman? Did I want to be the main woman?

"I never imagined our crushes going further than a few exciting encounters, but now our relationship feels more important to me than anything else." These vulnerable feelings were throwing me off-kilter. I was not used to being emotionally dependent. I felt helpless.

Sarah placed her hand flat above my heart. "Even when I'm not around, I'm still there." As tender a gesture as that was, it hadn't been enough. My wants, at that age, had been immediate.

"Do you love Linda more than you love me?" I removed a tissue from a box between the seats and wiped my tears.

"I love you both in different ways." Sarah's eyelids were rosy, her own tears not far away. She wasn't the same person from the summer. Both of us were different now. Two strong, confident women hiding in a cemetery with no ideas on how to proceed. "You fulfill something in me no one ever has," Sarah added. But that wasn't an answer. At least not the one I wanted to hear.

"That's the thing. You don't just fulfill something in me, you fulfill everything."

"That can't be true, Blu. You have so much going for you. You're young, smart, beautiful." Her flattery made it worse. "Look, we didn't plan for this to happen. I can't beat myself up because seeing you makes me happy, hearing your voice makes my heart flip, and making love with you becomes the beautiful equivalent of 'hearing the grass grow and the squirrel's heart beat, and we should die of that roar which lies on the other side of silence.'"

"'As it is, the quickest of us walk about well wadded with stupidity.'" I finished the passage from George Eliot's *Middlemarch*, another past assignment.

"Correct." Sarah beamed. "I wish somehow we could watch autumn go down together with all flags flying in glorious New England technicolor."

"We are watching autumn go down." I nodded to the windshield, now covered with leaves.

"At least we don't have to say goodbye. You're still coming tonight, right?"

I was. I'd become a glutton for punishment.

I followed Sarah's car in the dimming daylight past rows of corn fields and homes weathered from tough New England winters. She parked behind the Village Commons in South Hadley, and I pulled up beside her. The moment I got out, Sarah kissed me, saying she didn't want to end the night without doing that in case she didn't get the chance after the reading. Desire flooded through me, but apprehension replaced it. Had anyone seen us? And by anyone, I meant Linda.

Walking up to Fedora's, Sarah told me she'd found Linda crying in the sunroom that morning. Linda had sensed something was going on, and said Sarah's voice changed when she talked to me on the phone. Sarah had admitted she had a crush on me, and when Linda had said she couldn't understand how, considering the age difference, Sarah had pointed out that the age difference was exactly what made it not a threat, since it was improbable.

I knew Sarah had said "improbable" to throw Linda off our trail, but hearing our relationship described as improbable was a reminder of why I feared people finding out about us. Improbable meant unbelievable, impossible—words used to describe shock. I was falling in love and the only way to describe it was disbelief. Was it any wonder I looked upon our union with shame?

Sarah and I stopped outside the restaurant. Women entered and exited, and each time the door opened, loud voices drifted outside, only to go silent when the door closed. The air had turned cooler, the sky a Prussian blue.

"Linda asked me where you slept the night you organized our closet. I explained it had been too cold in the guest room and that I'd forgotten to turn on the space heater. She asked why I hadn't told her, and I said because it wasn't a big deal. Then she asked me if I wanted her to move out."

That halted me—and my heart. How had the situation become so complicated so soon? Either Sarah and I weren't good at keeping our secret, or Linda was more astute than we'd given her credit for.

"What did you tell her?" I hugged myself to ward off a chill.

"I told her she'd never have to move out."

"It's probably a bad idea for me to stay at your house tonight. I can go to my sister's dorm."

"No, it's fine." Sarah opened the door for me. "I promised Linda I wouldn't tell you about our discussion, so just act normal."

Normal? How was I to do that?

The entrance to Fedora's was crammed with people waiting to be seated. As the hostess led us to our table, Sarah stopped to shake hands with several women. It was like walking alongside the mayor.

Linda, Nan, and Connie were already seated. Sarah and I sat on the end, across from each other. Connie gave me a warm smile, Nan gave me a funny look, and Linda stared at my chest. Was she looking for evidence? A cat hair on my sweater? I wanted to squeeze myself down a black hole.

"How's your girlfriend?" Linda asked me right off the bat.

"We broke up," I said, realizing that made this situation seem worse. It didn't help that Sarah's foot, out of its shoe, was riding up my leg. "But I'm dating someone new. We play together in a basketball league." I blathered on. Sarah's foot froze, as did her expression. Did she think I was telling the truth?

"How was your golf game?" Sarah asked Linda, steering the conversation into another lane.

"Won by two," Linda said. "Plus I got restaurant recommendations for Key West."

"Oh, right, you're going down next week for your anniversary," Nan said to Linda, though looking at me.

"What's the traditional gift for thirteen?" asked Connie.

"Lace." Linda rested her hand over Sarah's on the table. After a beat, Sarah inched her hand away and scratched her nose, smiling at me as if to assure me Linda's gesture meant nothing. But that display of affection meant everything. Why hadn't Sarah told me about their anniversary? And were they staying at a hotel listed in the *Women's Traveler* book she'd just given me? Jealousy, surprise, and disappointment fell on me at once. I inched my chair back and Sarah's foot slipped away. I needed to protect myself starting right then and there.

After dinner we walked across the street onto the serene campus of Mount Holyoke College, dotted with enormous brick buildings, green manicured lawns, and towering elm trees. Mary E. Woolley Hall, an ornate structure with two enormous columns flanking the entrance, was named for the college's eleventh president, who, Sarah informed me, had lived with a female professor during her thirty-six-year tenure.

Sarah and I perused Adrienne Rich's books in the lobby while the others found seats. Sarah bought two copies of *What Is Found There*—one for herself and one for me.

I picked up a flier of upcoming local events and saw that Cris Williamson was coming to the Iron Horse. I'd played her song "Waterfall" so many times last summer, Sarah had banned it from the office. I asked Sarah if she'd like to go, but she said she and Linda had already gotten tickets and didn't ask me to join as she'd done with tonight's event. Pain bloomed in my abdomen.

Inside the concert hall I gazed around at all the women. "The Lebanese have come out of the woodwork," I whispered. It was Sarah's code word for lesbian, which she began using after an episode of the *Golden Girls* when Blanche had mixed up the two words.

"Adrienne is our Pied Piper," Sarah said.

I'd never heard of Adrienne Rich, nor read any of Emily Dickinson's poetry, until I met Sarah. The only poets I'd been familiar with were Shel Silverstein and Dr. Seuss.

We walked down our row to our seats. Sarah sat beside Linda, and I sat on Sarah's other side. Rich approached the lectern to applause. The petite poet smiled, and in her steady, expressive voice transformed the crowd into one listener. Calm overtook me. Partly from Rich's soothing words and partly from Sarah's thigh, hidden underneath her coat, pressed against my own.

We returned to Sarah's house after the reading. Linda had gone straight into their bedroom to watch the World Series, and Sarah and I spread blankets on the floor in the living room.

"I'm sorry Linda forgot to heat the guest room." Sarah tucked the edges of the blanket in around me.

"Why didn't you tell me about Key West?" I whispered.

"I was planning to tell you, because Linda is staying on a few extra days to visit friends. She always does this when we go away, since I have to come back for work. My idea was that you would come here, and we could spend a few days together." The prospect of a night with Sarah made me forget the evening's drama. "And remember." Sarah pressed her palm to my chest. "I might be in the other room, but I'm still there."

Sarah went into the bedroom and closed the door. The faint glow of the television seeped through the French doors' sheer fabric covering. One of my legs felt warmer than the other. I lifted my head and saw Cody nestled in beside me. Resting my head back down, I tried to make out the hushed but animated voices coming from the bedroom. What the hell was I doing? I sighed. I was doing whatever I could to be near Sarah.

~

Sarah and I headed out early the next morning for the UMass alumni golf tournament at Cherry Hill. I was paired with Evan, the former head counselor and current green dean, whose more important title was Kimberly's roommate. Sarah and I had hoped to be paired together, but just as well. Rachel would've observed us as though we were teenagers at a Catholic school dance.

"How is she?" I steered the cart to the second hole.

"She's finally getting out of bed." Evan squeezed the brim of his baseball hat. "She didn't for a week."

"It probably won't make a difference, but please tell Kimberly I still care about her." As wrapped up in Sarah as I was, Kimberly would forever be my first girlfriend and always hold a unique place in my heart.

Sarah suggested we blow off the alumni lunch, and we drove to the top of Mount Sugarloaf. On the deck of the observation tower, we felt anonymous among the leaf-peeping tourists gazing out at the foliage of the Happy Valley. Sarah wanted to take my picture, so I walked to the railing, which is when I spotted Sarah's secretary.

"Peg!" I figured better to play it cool than try to hide. Sarah motioned for Peg to get in the picture.

"I took a long lunch." Peg sidled up to me. "Think the rooster'll punish the hen?"

I put my arm around her. "Wouldn't worry about it."

Sarah told Peg to take the afternoon off. Peg winked at me, but Sarah was the one who had the ulterior motive. We drove to admissions, and Sarah said to the two student workers they could leave for the afternoon. Then we went into her office, and she locked the door.

After sharing a plate of pasta at Pinocchio's, our favorite Italian restaurant in Amherst, Sarah and I returned to her house. Linda was in bed watching television. I walked into the bedroom and, acting as though my spending the day with her girlfriend wasn't out of the ordinary, asked, "How was your golf tournament?"

"Good. We won. Four strokes." Linda did not look at me.

"That's awesome. Sarah says you're good enough to play in the LPGA." Praise spewed from my mouth as I stifled the urge to tell her she had nothing to worry about, that Sarah wouldn't break up with her, that it wasn't what we wanted. Instead, I said good night and went into the guest room, where Sarah waited to tuck me in. Linda had remembered to turn on the space heater.

The next morning, Sarah woke me with a kiss on each eyelid. "I'm off to the Saturday info session. There's juice for you on the counter. Linda's still sleeping." She shut off the space heater and left. I put the couch back together, folded the blankets, and took a shower.

"Are you still friendly with your ex?" Linda asked when I came out of the bathroom, dressed. She was seated at the counter in a bathrobe, hands wrapped around a mug of coffee, bags under her eyes. Was her haggard appearance the direct result of what she suspected Sarah and I were doing? Up to that point, I'd thought of Linda as an outside character in my story. Not as someone with her own story, one that also revolved around Sarah. Sarah was the one we each loved and the one who was—although I didn't see it at the time—hurting us both.

"Kimberly says she needs time, but I miss her. She was my best friend."

"They usually are." Linda had a distant look, as if she were talking to herself. As if I weren't even there.

"Are you dating Sarah?" Jackie's eyes rested on me as she waited for the truth. Hearing her state this fact I thought so dire, made my forkful of scrambled eggs unappealing. We'd snagged a table at Daisy's, a popular diner near campus. The noise level was high enough I'm sure no one heard her, but I glanced around anyway for possible listeners.

"What are you talking about?"

"Felice, I'm not stupid." Jackie bit into her toast. "At the concert, I saw how she stared at you. And you stay at her house every time you're here. I don't care if you're dating a woman. I just want you to be happy. Why can't you tell me? What's the big deal?"

The big deal was that my younger sister had just blurted out nonchalantly what I had been trying to hide, not just from the world, but from myself. Did she not think my being with Sarah was wrong? If she could so easily accept our age-gap love, would others? Maybe, but I couldn't accept it. Not then. Not for a long time. My fear of what others thought ruled my existence.

"Okay," I said. "Yes, we are seeing each other, but since Sarah has a girlfriend no one can know. Promise you won't tell Mom and Dad."

Jackie nodded. "I promise."

After breakfast we walked through campus. An enormous tent had been erected near Memorial Hall in preparation for an alumni event that evening. Along the Campus Pond, students were setting up tables and booths for a festival. A man dressed as a clown was juggling bowling pins. Jackie went into the tower library to study, and I walked over to the Campus Center.

A crowd of high school seniors and their parents were outside the auditorium gathering materials. Had it just been two years ago I was a student working these Saturday info sessions? I saw a group of former summer counselors huddled by the base of the escalators, waiting to lead campus tours, and approached them.

"You're all clumping." I poked my head into their circle. When they saw I wasn't Sarah, their nervous expressions turned to relief. Kimberly looked down at her feet.

Soon Sarah emerged from the auditorium, having delivered her introduction-to-the-university talk. Despite her tailored suit and fixed smile, her eyelids were pinkish. Something was wrong. She motioned for me to follow her behind the escalators, away from the diminishing crowd. We sat on one of many empty couches, far enough apart so as not to look suspicious if anyone walked by. I rested one bent leg between us.

"Linda's talking of moving out." Sarah placed her hand on the couch cushion, the tips of her fingers inches from my knee.

"Why?"

"Nan called Linda yesterday and said she'd seen us in Northampton looking cozy together."

I thought of my dream from the summer, when Sarah had come to my apartment to tell me Linda had left her and then kissed me. I'd never shared the dream with Sarah. Seeing how upset she looked now, I figured there was still no point in telling her.

"How is it any of Nan's business?"

"Nan and Linda dated a long time ago, and I've always suspected Nan still had feelings."

"Why did they break up?"

Sarah shrugged. "Probably lesbian bed death."

"What's that?" I asked as a male student walked by pushing a ten-speed bicycle.

"It's what they call it when the intimacy goes away in some long-term lesbian relationships, either from one person or both, and they stop having sex."

"Am I a distraction from your lesbian bed death?"

"What? Blu, no. I was okay with how things were with Linda. She's my family. You're my—" Sarah placed her hand on my knee. Anyone walking by would see. Fear made me pull my knee away. "Anyway." Sarah picked lint off her pants. "I don't think it's a smart idea for you to sleep over again. I'll get you a hotel room."

"It's Homecoming weekend; there's nothing available. But I can stay with my sister—who knows about us, by the way."

Sarah's head jerked up. "Did you tell her?"

"What, are you nuts? No, she figured it out. Guess we're not as inconspicuous as we'd hoped."

"You might be right." Sarah sighed. "There is some good news. Linda said she needed time to think and drove up to Vermont to visit friends. She won't be home until tonight, so what do you say we pick up tuna grinders from Bell's Pizza and—"

"I'm meeting friends at the game, remember?" I said. Sarah's eyelids grew pinker.

"It's the feel-good writer!" Lauren, my old editor, jumped up from her beach chair outside the football stadium. Even though the game had started, tailgaters with their portable seats, portable stoves, and portable radios still packed the lot. "I have good news and bad news. Did you hear about Tricia?"

"She finally took off her leather jacket?"

"She has a brain tumor and has been in the hospital since Labor Day. She's lost her memory and has less than a year to live."

"But she was going to write for *Rolling Stone*." I thought about my whining over the past few months, feeling frustrated with too many choices, and here was my friend, whose only choice was to accept her fate. What a spoiled brat I was.

"I know. But the good news is. . ." Lauren flashed her diamond ring. "Charlie and I got engaged." Lauren had begun dating Charlie freshman year and had always talked of getting married. I was surprised how soon after college they were going through with it. "Will you be my bridesmaid?"

"I'd love to," I lied, picturing myself walking down an aisle in front of a horde of people while wearing a fluffy, chiffon dress.

Friends kept arriving. Everyone asked each other, "What are you doing now?" The answers varied: newspaper reporter, student in graduate school, coffee shop barista. Some would add, "Just until I figure out my next move." Hearing their similar rocky transitions put me at ease, assuring me that this process of figuring out what I should be doing might take time.

At halftime we headed in to watch the marching band. I spotted Rachel at the alumni tent handing out water bottles. We hadn't spoken since our lunch the month before. I wanted to say hello but wasn't up for a lecture.

The stands were packed with people dressed in maroon and white, the UMass colors. I was enjoying the band's performance when I felt a hand on my shoulder. I turned to see Ben's goofy smile. Ben had been the opinion editor when I'd started submitting op-ed pieces my freshman year. After graduation he'd moved to New York City to write for a newspaper, and though he grew up in a small town, he said he felt at home in the city.

"I've been considering moving to New York," I said as we jumped up with the crowd when the UMass football players ran onto the field.

"If you do, let me know. My editor's always in search of freelance writers. She'd like your style."

"You think so?" My confidence had recently taken a downturn thanks to my growing collection of rejection letters.

"Felice, the city could use a feel-good writer." He pulled a business card from his back pocket. "Send me a few pieces and I'll show her."

There it was: a glimmer of optimism peeking through my otherwise murky future.

~

After the game a bunch of us went to the Old Amherst Ale House. It felt good to be among friends, a camaraderie I'd missed since graduation.

Peter, a childhood friend of Lauren's, sat beside me. His ruddy cheeks looked as though he'd been running in the cold and made him look boyish. We chatted and quickly discovered we'd both been roped into being in the wedding party.

"At least you can rent a tux. Who knows how much this dress will cost me?" I whispered.

"Yes, but you can wear it again," Peter said.

"You must not go to many weddings. I'll get as many uses from my dress as Lauren gets from hers."

"You're funny." He lifted his pint of beer. "Where do you live?"

"For now, with my parents on Cape Cod."

"Don't you mean Cape Cahd? Those accents kill me. How come you don't have one?"

"My mom's from Brooklyn and my dad's from Boston, so they canceled each other out. Where do you live?"

He wiped foam from his lip. "Outside of Boston. I work in finance. What about you?"

"I want to be a writer, but for now I'm working at my dad's law firm. Sometimes I go into Boston to file cases in Government Center."

"My office is across the street." His cheeks seemed to grow redder. "Maybe next time you come in we could get lunch."

Was he asking me out? I noticed the clock over the bar. Linda would be home soon. "Would you excuse me for a minute?" I walked to the pay phone in the back.

"Blu!" Sarah exclaimed when she answered. "I'm so glad you called. Come over."

"Won't Linda be home soon?"

"No, she's staying over in Vermont. I told you another opportunity would present itself." The prospect of spending the night in Sarah's arms sent butterflies loose inside me, but they were soon caged.

"What if Linda comes home during the night?"

"Don't worry. I know her."

I hung up and found Lauren waiting for me at the bar. "Do you like Peter? He asked me for your number."

I wanted to laugh at the absurdity. I'd just gotten off the phone with a woman I was having an affair with and was now learning that some guy was into me.

"Can I give it to him?" Lauren pressed.

"Okay," I said, knowing how persistent she could be. Truth was, I was attracted to Peter. Was it possible to be attracted to a man and a woman at the same time?

Sarah was standing at the stove, stirring a spoon around a saucepan, when I walked into her house. Frank Sinatra was singing and cats were roaming around. I dropped my overnight bag by the door and rushed to Sarah. She wrapped one arm around me, and I understood what Ben meant when he said he felt at home in New York. I felt at home with Sarah.

"Are you sure Linda won't come home tonight?" I asked, sitting at the counter.

"I'm sure. She called a little while ago from Vermont. I told her I was confused, and she bought it. But it's you that worries me. How are you feeling, Blu?"

"I feel bad because Linda feels bad."

"Maybe I shouldn't tell you this stuff." Sarah resumed stirring. "It's not your problem."

"How's it not my problem? If it weren't for me, Linda wouldn't need to think."

"If it weren't for you, I wouldn't have this pleasure here." Sarah placed her right hand over her heart. "When Linda said she wasn't coming home, my first thought was you could sleep over. I know it's not right, but it's what I want. Rachel has a theory that these things happen when there's a space that isn't being filled by current relationships."

"Does that mean Rachel's coming around?" Cody jumped up onto the stool next to me. I stroked his head and he squeezed his eyes shut.

"No, she thinks I should work things out with Linda. I explained that I'd become okay with those spaces and wasn't looking to fill them. That this was person-specific and grew from the love you and I share. I admit sometimes I have this crazy urge to tell Linda the truth, but then reality sinks in, and it wouldn't be fair to you. You need someone your own age. I hate to hurt you both, and it seems that's all I'm doing."

As happy as I was with Sarah, I didn't want to be the reason for her breaking up with Linda, especially since I still wasn't comfortable claiming membership in the Lesbian Club (present situation excluded). As our affair remained secret, so too did my sexuality, which was why, at least in some part, being the other woman, despite its obvious limitations, worked for me.

Maybe "worked for me" was stretching it. Accepting the role and restrictions came at the expense of my own happiness.

Sarah removed two cans of cat food from a cabinet and handed them to me. "Mind feeding the cats?"

I emptied the cans onto two small dishes. Cody jumped down from the stool, Archie and Maxi crept over from the living room, and Sammy waddled in from the bedroom. Pavlov's cats.

"How was it seeing your friends at the game?" Sarah brought her reading glasses down from atop her head and flipped the page of her recipe book.

"My friend Lauren asked me to be a bridesmaid at her wedding in April." I tossed the cans into the recycling bin and washed my hands. "And another friend offered me a potential writing job."

"Around here?" Sarah looked at me over the rims of her glasses. My stomach got that happy sensation it did whenever she gazed at me that way.

"New York City. Wouldn't that be awesome?"

"But do you want to live in New York City?"

"Why not? Millions of people do." I sat back down at the counter.

"Exactly." Sarah spooned bowtie pasta, artichoke hearts, and tuna onto two blue Fiesta dishes.

"Sarah, you're the one who said opportunities don't appear, that I need to make them happen. And now one has. The only writing not being rejected is in my journal and my letters to you, and who'd want to read that? I want to be a writer, not organize closets for the rest of my life."

"Don't be so melodramatic." Sarah set down the dishes. "With your skills, you could run a company."

"But I don't want to run a company; I want to be a writer."

"And I want to be a lounge singer, but until you reach your goal, you need to support yourself." Sarah sat beside me. "You're great at organizing. It gives you structure and satisfaction, and sometimes that's all you can hope for."

Was adulthood all about practicality?

"Are you trying to dissuade me from striving for my dreams?"

"No, I'm trying to arm you with reality." Sarah rested her hand on mine. "Your friend's offer sounds promising, and I support you. But you said the city scared you."

"It does a little, but the sacrifice seems worth the exposure a column in the city would give me."

"Sacrificing your safety for your career?"

"Now who's being melodramatic?" I slid my hand away and picked up my fork. "Maybe if I had my career settled, then my real life could follow."

"Your real life?"

"My love life." I pierced the fork into an artichoke heart. Sarah's jaw tightened. Had I meant to hurt her? "I get why my friend is getting married so soon. It's scary as hell out here all alone."

"You're not alone. You've got me."

"I don't have you. Linda has you. And this"—I waved the fork with the artichoke on the end between us—"isn't real. You already have a life with someone." Did I want a life with Sarah? Every time I thought of us being together, I imagined my parents' disappointment, certain they'd think I was throwing my life away, missing out on rites of passages only available to young people who married other young people. "If you loved me, then—" I stopped. Then what? Sarah would leave Linda to be with me? Or break up with me and set me free? Neither answer was one I was ready to handle.

"I do love you, Blu. And I have those same dreams and fears. I know this situation isn't fair to you. You have so much to look forward to, and I don't want to get in the way. But my feelings for you are real. We have tonight. And when I get back from Key West, we'll have two more nights together. Plus, how can we forget our long weekend in September? We'll always have that."

"But I'm twenty-three. I don't want my happiest moments to be behind me."

"Take it from me, having memories is better than not having them." Sarah pointing out that I still had my whole life ahead of me to create more memories, while she was cherishing each as if it might be her last, only emphasized our age difference.

I stared at Sarah. Was she a distraction from me starting my real life or was she meant to be part of it? My focus should've been on my career, but my energies were zapped from my constant longing for her and the endless worry about people finding out about us. Why did our love have to be controversial? When Lauren and Charlie announced their intention to marry, the world embraced it. I thought if Sarah and I made that same announcement, the world would balk.

"I think we should break things off for a while," I said, a knee-jerk reaction.

Sarah flinched. "You want to end it cold turkey?"

"Maybe cold tuna." I nodded to the plate, trying to inject some humor. "We can write but not talk. I need to figure things out."

"It's your decision."

Was it?

We started to eat, but by now the food was no longer hot.

"Cold tuna." Sarah sighed. "It's a sign."

"How's your social life on the Cape?" Peter asked. We were sitting beneath the dome of Faneuil Hall Marketplace in Boston, where Sam Adams had encouraged independence from Great Britain over two hundred years before. Now it was the largest food hall in New England, where chefs encouraged people to try their wares using the aroma of meats and sweets.

"I'm sorry, social life? What's that?" I spoke loudly to be heard over the deafening sound of tourists and holiday music.

He laughed as he ripped off the edge of his sourdough bread bowl and dunked it, soaking up the last of his clam chowder. "Lauren said you were a popular columnist at UMass. Who do you write for now?"

"A local paper, but I'm waiting to hear from an editor in New

York City about a freelancing job."

"Does that mean you'd move there?"

"Maybe. But I'd first need to get a real job. Rent's expensive." A toddler ran by our table, his face covered in chocolate, his mother trailing him, her hands full of napkins.

"Do you have any of your income directly deposited into a savings account?" He put the chunk into his mouth.

I spooned up soup, keeping my eyes on him. "And what income would that be?"

He laughed. "Even ten bucks a week adds up."

"My grandfather would love you."

"Just your grandfather?"

I smiled at the implication, certain I was blushing. "Where do you live?"

"Brighton. I bought a multi-family house last year. I live in one apartment and rent out the other two. I'd invite you over, but my place is a mess, and Lauren said you organize closets. I've never heard of anyone doing that."

"You'd be surprised how many people need help organizing their stuff."

"No, I get it. Maybe next time?"

"Sure." I checked my watch. A little after four. I pictured Sarah sitting by her phone, hoping I'd call. We hadn't spoken since I'd left her place the week before. "I should get going. Basketball game tonight."

Peter picked up both of our trays. "Are you a Celtics fan? My company has season tickets if you'd like to go to a game."

"I'd love to."

We walked along State Street and Peter took my hand. It felt strong and secure. Then there was Sarah's hand, a third the size. When she held mine, I felt a similar comfort.

At South Station I thanked him again for the soup. Peter smiled and without warning, kissed me. It startled me. Not the kiss as much as the realization that it was the most public display of affection I'd ever been a part of. I glanced around at the tide of Bostonians heading home after work. No one looked our way. No one, I realized, cared.

~

November 8, 1993

Blu-

A hard fist of reality twists at my heart
Breathing becomes a series of odd
Imperceptible catches
Two weeks of silence,
Two weeks of 4:00 p.m. telephone calls missed
Two weeks of Southwest sunsets, gone in unaccustomed
Silence
How not to wonder or worry or care?
How did we get—so soon—from there to here?

It's 4:00 p.m. Silent time, sunset onset time, our time. I'm listening to BS in yet another publications meeting, trying to appear interested but am instead writing you a letter because I need a little Felice. This beautiful season has lost its center. My world has flipped over. The smiles and touches of September and October seem part of that magic crazy time that lives in a time capsule to be remembered and valued for itself alone. No matter how wonderful our times now are or have been, they seem to fade off in the mix of current confusion and uncertainty. And now memories have blurred edges like end pages of a four-carbon copy. Wish we could live with sharper edges and watch this November go down together and not go down with it. This month is a major all-time low for me. Everything dies. We didn't know what to do with this crush when it began. Now it's beyond crush and I know even less. Is this where we get realistic and admit we're on a treadmill going nowhere and should save ourselves from ourselves? I don't know. What I do know is, I'm still there. S.

November 11, 1993

Sarah,

I keep thinking, "just end it," since dragging it out won't let us get on with our lives, but the thought of never seeing you again is worse. At first, I chalked this up as another lesson to learn from you, but somehow it has proceeded further than anything I imagined. How did we let it? Or did we not have a choice? I've never had the impulse to say, "I love you" to anyone. Except now, with you. Those September days were a dream come true, but now we face a "realer" reality. We're miles apart, years apart, and we can only talk to Mark (who supports us) and Rachel (who does not). I'm exhausted, but sleep remains out of reach, which is a bummer because sleep is when I picture us together. All I can do is write, sift through memories, and hope for more love to come. You're right. November is extra dark and bland without you in it. ♥Blu

November 15, 1993

Blu,

It was a lonely, Felice-less weekend. I wanted to look over and find you on the couch smiling back at me. I stopped by the parking office to renew my sticker and Brenda told me of an upcoming higher education conference at MIT next month. That's one I could "attend." Want to meet me? There's another in March. Yes, it's far away, but it's another chance to be together. Then there's always any day. I hate this, but no matter how crazy, it happened. Our miracle. S.

November 18, 1993

Sarah,

It's 4:14 p.m. Our time. I dread this hour, knowing we should be talking on the phone. Time is such a major theme between us. Not enough time together, too much time between visits. Even though you say I have so much time ahead of me, I often feel strapped for time as though I'm losing it, or worse, wasting time I could be spending finding my purpose. Time feels like my enemy, passing me by and I have nothing to show for it. Mark says I put too much pressure on myself. If you were here you'd block these irrational thoughts from crossing my mind. Which is why I need you. Sometimes I wonder why you need me. ♥Blu

In the past month my emotions had gone from hopeful (imagining my future with Sarah) to regret beyond repair (imagining my future without Sarah). I tried to focus on my job prospects as a writer, sending my best articles to Ben's editor, yet my days were lonely with no 4 p.m. phone calls. After a month of no verbal communication with Sarah, so I could "figure things out," what I figured out was that I missed her. Terribly. Even though Sarah swore her love in her letters, my head filled with irrational thoughts. Was she no longer interested in me? Was she making love to Linda? And if so, was she whispering to Linda the same reminder to breathe? What made these questions so incessant was that I had nothing positive to focus on. Responses from editors were encouraging, but no job offers. Sarah would've put things in perspective, but every time I picked up the phone to call her, I dialed my uncle instead. Until one night, sitting in my bedroom, working on a jigsaw puzzle, I had a moment of weakness.

"Yes," Sarah answered, her voice abrupt, as though the only person to call her home at that hour would be a telemarketer.

"It's me."

"What's up?"

What's up? Linda must be nearby.

"I needed to hear your voice." I tried not to let her coolness derail my simple motive: touch base and restabilize my irrational thoughts.

"Call me at work tomorrow," Sarah said, making believe she was talking to a coworker. "Then I can check my file."

"But—"

"Great. Thanks." Sarah hung up.

She hung up!

I called Mark for the third time that day. "I can't keep doing this," I whined. "Why is this so hard?"

"What happened?" Referee whistles blared in the background. He must've been watching the New York Knicks.

"Sarah hung up on me because Linda was there."

The noise in the background stopped. "If Linda moved out tomorrow, would you want to move in with Sarah?"

"No."

"You sound sure," Mark said. I was far from sure. "Maybe you should end things before it's too late."

"But what if it's true love? I've never cried over anyone. Doesn't that mean something?"

"The key word in that sentence is 'true.' The lies you two have been telling cancel that out." Silence while I chewed that thought. "Felice, what is it you want?"

"To not have to share her. Aside from you, I can only share

Sarah with my journal. And when I see it in black and white, it's worse."

"Then stop writing in your journal."

"What? I can't. If I don't write it down, I'll forget. And when that memory fades, it'll be as though I never had that experience, and my life won't have meaning or something. When I'm not writing, I'm distracting myself by organizing closets and doing puzzles."

"My closets could use some organizing."

"Your closets could always use some organizing." I hung up and continued working on my thousand-piece jigsaw puzzle. After I'd put the edge pieces together, I felt better. I had accomplished something. Productivity: my go-to remedy to avoid the problem at hand.

After leaving Dad's office the next day, I drove to the beach. I had a free hour until I had to pick up Meredith from karate.

The sand was stiff beneath my boots, and I bent my head against the cold December wind, the salty air pricking my face. On the water, whitecaps curled up in rows. I climbed the lifeguard tower and stared at the ocean, which appeared as vast and directionless as my future.

In the distance, sitting on the skyline, a ferry was travelling back to Hyannis from Nantucket or Martha's Vineyard. Further along the shore, a black Labrador chased seagulls, its owner so bundled up I couldn't tell if it was a man or woman. And there, in the center of the parking lot, the bathhouse. At one end, showerheads. At the other, a payphone. I jumped down onto the hard sand.

"Sarah," she answered, quick and to the point.

"It's me."

"Blu! I was debating taking the chance to call you at home."

"I'm still upset about you hanging up on me last night."

"I'm so sorry about that, but I can't talk when Linda's home. It places me in an uncomfortable position, not to mention puts our situation at risk."

What was our situation?

"I thought it would be better not to talk to you," I said, "but I've missed you."

"Me too. I'm trying to work but am instead watching images of you floating through my head. Is there a word for this beyond crush?"

"Crushed." I was mad at myself for calling. So weak.

"If it's any consolation, I'm not eating again," Sarah said. "And I can't get any work done. On my drive in this morning, I heard Kenny's song "Only a Miracle" and had to pull over until I stopped crying."

That made two of us.

Out on the beach a seagull had perched atop the lifeguard tower, its body outlined by the pale-blue sky. Beyond, the sun began its early descent.

"How's the writing?" Sarah broke the silence.

"Turns out I've misplaced my motivation. I doubt I'll ever achieve anything."

"Emily Dickinson said, 'Success is counted sweetest by those who never succeed.'"

"Is that supposed to cheer me up?" I huddled closer to the bathhouse, letting it block a gust of wind.

"Blu, I get it. You're frustrated because you're so damn task-oriented. That's part of what I love about you. But you're doing the right thing. You're writing for that newspaper and improving your skills. Success doesn't materialize overnight. Everything you want will happen. Just keep moving."

"The only moving I'm doing is my little sister, from one activity to another. I hate my life."

"Whining."

"Bite me."

"Listen," Sarah said. "I wish we could take a trip together where the time goes more slowly and—"

"Why do you always talk about us taking trips? We've only been together once outside of the Happy Valley. Who knows, maybe this is a geographical affair, sustainable only *inside* the Happy Valley. Maybe that's what makes it so happy."

"Okay," Sarah said, "let's put your location theory to the test."

"How?"

"I mentioned to Linda that conference next weekend in Boston. She didn't bat an eye. I thought you could meet me, and then we'd go to the Cape. You can show me where you grew up."

"What do I tell my parents?"

"Tell them I was in Boston and needed your input for next summer's orientations, and you invited me to visit. Call me tomorrow morning and we can go over the plans."

"I can't. Rachel told me not to use the alumni's number anymore. I just used it now, so I'm sure she'll give me a hard time about it."

"She mentioned that, but I had an idea. When you're home alone, call my direct number and hang up after one ring. I'll know it's you from the off-campus double ring and call you back. This way it won't show up on your parents' phone bill."

That was Sarah, always thinking, always a step ahead, a trait I would myself perfect, realizing, only too late, its real intention: deceit.

"I've got an appointment for a biopsy Friday," Sarah said the next day, after I'd used our one-ring signal. "Then I'll head to Boston."

"Biopsy for what?"

"My gynecologist found something and wants to check it out. Don't worry. I've got impeccable genes. My mom lived into her eighties, and my aunt's going to be ninety. I'm sticking around for a while." Hearing Sarah talk about doctors reminded me of the conversations my grandparents and their friends have when sitting around the pool in Florida. Before I could respond, someone picked up another phone in my house.

"I'm on the phone," I said, praying Sarah wouldn't let out a peep.

"Sorry, honey," Mom said before hanging up. I said bye to Sarah and ran downstairs.

"Who were you talking to?" Mom removed a cereal box from one of several grocery bags. Her shoulder-length brown hair had been blown out and her makeup was flawless. She was wearing a black sweater and black pants. "You can take the girl out of Brooklyn," she was fond of saying, "but you can't take Brooklyn out of the girl." True, considering she'd been living on Cape Cod, birthplace of pink and green, longer than she'd lived in Brooklyn.

"Mom, in the last five years I haven't had to tell anyone who I'm talking to on the phone." I aligned the cereal boxes in the pantry by height. "Can you please give me a little privacy?"

"I'm sorry, honey. I'm just interested in your life."

But would she still be interested if she knew her daughter was having an affair with a card-carrying female member of AARP?

Mom fingered a lock of my hair. "Want me to make an appointment for you with Alfredo? He's great with curly hair."

I yanked my head back. "Are you saying my hair looks bad?" I was falling off the deep end.

"Of course not. What do you say we have a nice lunch and talk?" She held up a can of tuna. "You can tell me what's going on in your life." Had she heard me on the phone with Sarah? Or did she miss the closeness we'd used to share before I became this unsettled, on-edge clone of myself?

"No, thanks." Tuna reminded me of Sarah. I stormed outside to check the mailbox, my lifeline to the outside world—or rather, to Sarah. I ripped open a letter from a newspaper editor and scanned the brief note. "Thank you for your submission, but..."

Great, another rejection letter. I looked through the rest of the mail. Spotting Sarah's distinct handwriting soothed my nerves. Back in the kitchen, I said, "I'm sorry, Mom. Yes, I'd love to have a nice lunch with you, but only if it's egg salad."

She smiled, accustomed to my brand of sarcasm.

"I'm looking forward to Saturday," Peter said over the phone.

"I'm sorry," I said. "I'm not going to be able to make it."

"That's okay. I can switch the tickets. Can you come Tuesday?"

"Peter." I paused. "I think you're great, but I need to be honest. I started dating someone in September. We broke up for a few weeks and I thought it was over, but we just got back together."

"Oh." Defeat in his voice. "Well, I hope he's worthy of you."

Nestled in the front seat of the Plymouth & Brockton bus, my dad's briefcase containing legal documents beside me, I found the repetitive bare trees lining the Mid-Cape Highway, like endless sheep, lulling me to sleep. I woke an hour later to a row of shiny skyscrapers. The Boston skyline had blossomed over the years. The city where I'd been born had grown up.

~

After filing the legal documents, I took a taxi across the Charles River and sat inside MIT's student center, rereading the same page of my book, too excited to focus. Sarah soon appeared, looking refined in a navy blazer, white button-down shirt, and jeans, with a gray wool scarf around her neck. My eagerness grew as I watched her scan the room, knowing she was looking for me. When our eyes met, she smiled and headed toward me. As she got closer, my excitement turned to angst. Would the students think she was my mother? Why did that matter? When Sarah was within five feet, I noticed dark circles under her eyes. Was it the stress of our secret or the contrast to all the younger faces in the room?

"Your hair looks fantastic," Sarah said. "You look so grown up with it shorter."

"My mom broke me down."

"So, do I get a hug?" Sarah asked. Eyeing the room, I stood and put my arms around her.

"When did you start to wear Jovan?" I asked when we sat down, our thighs touching.

"When you weren't around to smell it on." Sarah removed a writing journal from her briefcase and handed it to me. Taped to the cover was a cutout of Emily Dickinson's face with red hearts drawn around her head and the words: "I love you with all my hearts." Inside she'd inscribed: "To Blu: Another lover of words. Sarah."

"Thank you." I leaned over to kiss her cheek, but Sarah turned her head, and my kiss landed on her lips. I pulled away and gazed around, my heart thumping fast. "Are you nuts? There are people here."

"People," Sarah said. "Who don't give a whit about us."

It was late afternoon when we crossed the Sagamore Bridge. The Cape Cod Canal, a dark-blue ribbon beneath us, flowed toward a pale-pink sunset. I rolled down my window and yelled over the rush of arctic air, "It's a family tradition to open the window every time we cross back onto the Cape! Smelling the salty air reminds us that we're home!"

"I do love a tradition!" Sarah rolled down her window, and we took great gulps of air until our noses were numb from the cold.

~

Fifteen minutes later Sarah pulled into the driveway at my parents' house. It was pitch black out, the sky full of stars. The air smelled cold, like snow was coming. I shuddered, but not from the temperature. Sarah was about to meet my parents, who thought they would be meeting my former boss, not my current lover. Would they figure it out just by looking at my face? I had never lied to them. I had never had a reason to.

We paused in front of the garage to kiss and a light flicked on, startling us. For a second, I thought my parents had been watching from a window, until I remembered that the light was on a sensor.

"We feel we already know you." Dad took Sarah's coat in the foyer. "Felice talks about you all the time."

"It's nice to finally meet you both. You have a wonderful daughter." Sarah handed Mom a gift. "A little thank you for having me."

"You shouldn't have." Mom led Sarah into the kitchen. On the counter was a platter of crudité and hummus. "We're the ones who are thankful. You've been such a great mentor."

Yeah, lesbian mentor!

"Did everything go well at the courthouse?" Dad asked me.

I nodded. "The receipts are in the briefcase."

"Great, thanks." He handed Sarah a glass of wine. "Felice says you're a golfer. Did she tell you what happened to me once on the golf course?"

"No, but I love a good golf story."

I rolled my eyes. "You'll love this one."

Dad's expression grew serious. "My friend Jim and I were on the fifth hole when he had a heart attack and dropped dead."

"That's terrible." Sarah's glass froze mid-air. "What did you do?"

"What could I do?" Dad threw up his hands. "I hit the ball. Dragged Jim. Hit the ball. Dragged Jim."

Sarah broke out in laughter. "Now I see where Felice gets her humor, among her many other talents."

I sipped my seltzer to hide the smile spreading out across my face, certain my expression would reveal everything.

"Felice was the best night director the program ever had," Sarah continued. "Aside from her organizing skills, she's an amazing leader and public speaker." It sounded as if I were back in high school on parents' night, teachers praising me, my parents beaming in response. Had that been the root of my attraction to Sarah? The way she gushed over me?

"Felice is a hard worker." Dad placed his hand on my shoulder. "I know once she figures out what she wants to do, whether it's run a company or write a *New York Times* bestseller, she'll be successful."

"I've no doubt." Sarah winked at me.

The nasal hum of sitar music and voices filled the Indian restaurant in Hyannis. Sarah and I followed the hostess to the only available table, and passed two couples, friends of my parents.

"Felice." One of the women reached for my hand, her eyes wandering to Sarah. I considered introducing Sarah, but what would I say? I'd like you to meet my secret, older, lesbian lover? "What are you doing now?" She sounded like the adults who interrogated Benjamin Braddock in *The Graduate*.

"Not plastics, that's for sure," I replied.

The wife looked confused, but both the husbands laughed.

"Well, I don't want to keep you from your chicken tikka. Good to see you." I continued to where the hostess stood waiting.

Once we sat, Sarah put on her reading glasses and opened her menu. "What do you recommend? I've never eaten Indian food."

"Really?"

"Guess I'm too addicted to Chinese."

I ordered our meal, pleased to introduce Sarah to something new. Sarah moved her glasses to the top of her head and rested her elbows on the table, tenting her fingers. "Listen, Blu. I've been thinking long and hard about us. You're trying to figure out your life, at least the next phase, and need to put your energies into your career. I support you. But we've only had a handful of days and nights together, and just as it all came to life, we tried to call it off and stop the miracle." Her foot found mine under the table. "I believe we have more to share and do together, and I think I found a way that allows us to do that. Instead of ending it cold tuna, and calling it off, we could try warm tuna, and continue to see each other without pressure. This relationship might not be everything you want, but it sure is some of what you want, isn't it?"

It was, but only because I couldn't have more. And I wanted more. More time with Sarah. More freedom to be together. More acceptance from others. But circumstances only allowed for more of the same, which was more than I had without her. I convinced myself it was enough.

"No wonder you're such an incredible organizer. You've had plenty of practice." Sarah stood inside the larger of my two closets. We had gone to the beach after dinner and had made out in my car, listening to the sound of the waves lapping the shore. By the time we came home, everyone was asleep. Sarah picked up a photo leaning against a basketball trophy. "Is that you with Larry Bird? You come up to his waist."

"I was ten when I went to his camp." I grabbed a sleeping bag from the top cubby and followed Sarah into the bedroom. I lay the sleeping bag on the floor, shut the lights, and climbed in the queen-sized bed beside Sarah.

"Get out," she said.

"What? Why?"

"Someone might come in."

"No one will come in. And you came all this way. Can't we at least sleep together?"

"I thought tomorrow we'd go to Provincetown and stay at a B&B."

"Really? You can stay another day?"

"It's a two-day conference," Sarah said. I kissed her, then dove into the sleeping bag, smiling so hard my cheeks hurt. Around midnight, Meredith came in and got into the sleeping bag with me.

"I told you someone might come in," Sarah whispered in the dark.

The next morning, while Sarah showered, I went down to the kitchen where my family was eating breakfast. It had occurred to me that my parents might have considered it strange Sarah had slept in my bedroom. When I had mentioned to Mom that Sarah would be staying over, she'd responded, "There are clean sheets on Jackie's bed." I'd replied, perhaps too quickly, "That's okay. She can sleep in my room."

Friends had always stayed in my room on sleepovers, and Sarah was, despite being older, a friend. Did her age make a difference? If it did, Mom hadn't said anything. But now that Sarah was there, I felt exposed, as though my parents could see through my lies.

"Meredith, did you have a bad dream last night? You kept kicking me in your sleep." I wanted my parents to know she'd slept in my room to dispel any contemplations.

Removing her hand from inside the cereal box, Meredith studied the small yellow plastic prize. "I don't remember."

"What are your plans today?" Mom asked me.

I plucked a strawberry off the silver-plated platter Sarah had given my mother. "After I help Sarah, I'm meeting friends off-Cape. I'll be back tomorrow morning." Lying, it appeared, had become effortless.

Sarah and I left my parents' house in separate cars. I parked mine at a hotel in Hyannis, figuring it would go unnoticed for the weekend, and then hopped into Sarah's car. As she drove along Route 6A, the scenic, curving road dotted with wide-trunked trees and rambling old homes built in the late 1600s, Sarah was excited to learn it was once a Native American trail and trade route.

Cruising the last stretch through Eastham, Wellfleet, and Truro, closed clam shacks and fudge shops reflecting winter's vast bareness, I opened my *Women's Traveler* book. "Here's a place with ocean views and homemade pastries."

"And hopefully a comfortable bed." Sarah took my hand. We were both wearing winter gloves. Our relationship had progressed to a new season.

Our B&B was a two-story white-clapboard house sandwiched between two others. Our top-floor room had a view of the Pilgrim Monument and the Cape Cod Bay. And because it was the off-season, we got a discount, which Sarah paid in cash.

I climbed under the heavy white comforter. It might have been noon, but we had catching up to do. "Did you know that the Pilgrim Monument commemorates the first stop for the

Mayflower Pilgrims? Not Plymouth?"

"I didn't." Sarah sat on the bed and removed her socks.

"Who'd have guessed one day I'd be gazing at it with my—" My what? Girlfriend? I coughed, pretending the reason for my hesitation was a tickle.

"Well." Sarah took me in her arms, our cool skin warming from contact. "Now it can commemorate our first vacation."

We made love without worries or distractions. Another first.

"See?" Sarah said when we woke from a nap. "We're connecting, and we're far from the Happy Valley."

"I could learn to love this," I purred, sheltered in her embrace. "It's better than what we usually watch."

"And what's that, Blu?"

"The clock."

Sarah sighed, her breath warm on my forehead. "You don't want that kind of relationship with me."

"What are you saying?" I inched up onto one elbow. "You're the one always talking about us taking trips together."

"Yes, I want to take trips with you, but you don't need a full-time girlfriend as you begin your life—especially an old one. In the long run, it's not fair to you."

"Let me get this straight. You're too old to openly do things with me, but you're not too old to secretly do them?"

"That's not what I meant. I don't want to hold you back from the rest of your life."

"But what if being with you is how I want to spend the rest of my life?"

Without responding, Sarah lowered me onto my back. Discussion tabled once again.

We spent the afternoon walking along Commercial Street, the one-lane street that cut through town, wandering into the few jewelry shops, sweatshirt stores, and art galleries open that time of year. Many store windows were lit up with Christmas decorations. Provincetown was quiet and unpopulated, nothing like summertime, when tourists and drag queens, inviting you to their impersonator shows, packed the streets, a kaleidoscope of characters. Of the few couples we saw, most held hands, this being the country's most gay-friendly community. Sarah kept reaching for mine, but I kept them planted in my pockets, accustomed to protecting our secret. I knew no other way.

At dusk, we entered Womencrafts, a shop that sold pottery, gifts, and jewelry handmade by women.

"Come." Sarah made a beeline to a wall of books. "More reading for your education. Let's start with the classics." She piled paperbacks into my arms. *Curious Wine, The Price of Salt, Oranges Are Not the Only Fruit, Rubyfruit Jungle.*

"These titles are making me hungry," I joked, placing the books by the register. Sarah walked over to the jewelry display. A minute later she held out two rings and asked which one I liked.

"You want my opinion on a ring for Linda?"

"No." Sarah shook her head. "For you."

I glanced at the saleswoman who was my age, had a buzz cut, and wore a T-shirt with "Lick Bush in '92" across the chest. I expected her jaw to drop, but she just smiled. Reassured, I chose a silver band with a white-and-teal design. Sarah slid it on my finger. Just like that.

Outside, the sun had set. The wind whipping off the bay made it colder, but I wore only one glove, which allowed me to gaze at the ring. Sarah reached for my other hand. Since it was dark, I let her take it. But soon I was gripped with an uneasiness. "Do you think the saleswoman thought, 'What an age difference?'"

"Blu, you need to stop caring what other people think."

How? Caring what other people thought was etched into my DNA, helped me measure my self-worth. Trophies, awards, newspaper write-ups—all tangible credentials that described the me on the outside. If the inside me were to be found out, I feared I would no longer measure up.

Sarah came out of the bathroom wrapped in a fluffy robe and picked up *The Diary of Emily Dickinson* I'd left on her pillow. She held the book at arm's length, since she wasn't wearing her glasses, and read my inscription: "'Diaries are books we fill with words we wish to share out loud. Love, Blu.' Thank you." Sarah put down the book, removed her robe and joined me under the covers. Her body, warm from the shower, filled the empty contours of my own. As we made love, it took all my concentration not to think about her leaving the next day.

"We should get on the road, Blu. They said it might snow." Sarah placed her blue-and-white toiletry bag into her suitcase. I remained under the covers and watched her pack. The sky was overcast and gray. On the dresser were two glasses of juice and a plate of scones.

"I hate this part." I curled onto my side. "Saying goodbye and not knowing when we'll see each other again."

Sarah sat beside me and rested her cool hand on my head. "I hate this part too."

We drove back to my car in silence. When we hugged, for the first time, Sarah let go before I did.

"How was your weekend?" Mom asked. She and Dad were reading in the living room, piano music playing on the stereo.

"Okay. Nice to see my friends. Didn't get much sleep," I mumbled as I lumbered upstairs.

Meredith was in her bedroom practicing karate moves in front of a mirror. She wore the blue UMass sweatshirt I'd given her, which reached her knees.

In my room, I lobbed my overnight bag, filled with the books Sarah had bought me, into a closet, turned on the stereo, and plunked down at my desk. Ann Reed began to sing, "If I told you the truth / If I let my heart sing / Would I then win your love / Or lose everything." Her words caused an ache in my chest, as though my heart were breaking. Tears appeared and I didn't bother wiping them away as I wrote in my journal everything that had happened since meeting Sarah in Boston. Writing absorbed my torment, my new current state of mind.

"Hey." Dad rested his hand on my back. I hadn't even heard him come into my room. "What's wrong?"

I didn't answer. I couldn't. I was hyperventilating. I'd gone from a non-crier to a human waterfall, the truth fighting its way out.

"Come," he said. We sat beside each other on the bed. He

wrapped his arm around me and I rested my head on his shoulder. "Are you upset because you're living at home?" he asked. I shook my head. "Is it because you don't have a job?" Another shake. "Is it," he hesitated, "your sexuality?"

My shoulders, tight from sobbing, popped up. "I think I might be gay. Mark says not to worry about labels and just do what makes me happy."

"Smart approach." Dad reached for the box of tissues beside my bed and handed it to me. "Sweetheart, whatever the situation, your mother and I support you. We've often talked about what qualities we'd want in a son-in-law, but we can adjust that to a daughter-in-law."

Why was it so easy for him to accept me when it was so hard for me to do the same?

I was dying to tell Sarah about my disclosure to Dad but had to wait until 4 p.m. the next afternoon. The waiting was excruciating.

"I came out to my dad," I said when Sarah called me back at 4:01.

"How'd your mom respond?"

"I haven't talked to her yet, but I'm sure Dad did." I opened a kitchen cabinet and removed four dinner plates. "They keep nothing from each other."

"Just know it's harder for mothers. They think we need men to take care of us. The bottom line is your mother loves you. Give her time."

"Did you get the results back from your biopsy report?" I set the plates onto the table.

"The doctor said I need a D and C and otherwise I should be fine."

"What's that? A dusting and cleaning?"

Laughing, Sarah said, "Close. The doctor's confident that once the procedure's over, I should have nothing to worry about."

I had offered (okay, jumped at the opportunity) to pick up Jackie at UMass and drive her home for winter break. Any excuse to see Sarah.

Sarah took me to dinner at Judie's. I was excited about the popover, but not as much as I was about Sarah's foot touching mine under the table. Afterward, we went to a men's basketball game at the new Mullins Center. During halftime, Rachel's boss, the director of Alumni Relations, greeted me by holding out his silk necktie. "Can you paint more of these? I've had alumni ask where they can buy them."

His maroon tie had the UMass logo in gold on the wide end with gold basketballs zigzagging up to the neck. It was one of two I'd hand-painted my senior year at the Student Union Craft Center. I'd given the other one to the chancellor when he'd invited me to his house for lunch with five other overachieving soon-to-be graduates.

"Sure," I said. "How many?"

"Let's start with a dozen."

A dozen! I might've been sitting in the stands, but on the inside, I was dancing a jig. I spent the second half of the game making a mental list of supplies I needed to buy. I couldn't wait to tell Dad, who'd been offering to convert the basement into a necktie factory. I wasn't quite ready to start a business, but I was excited to have another reason to get up in the morning.

Rachel and others headed to Rafters Sports Bar after the game. Sarah had to get home but asked me to sit in her car for a minute. I was only in town one night, so I was annoyed she'd put Linda's needs ahead of mine and said no. Then I spent the entire time at Rafter's riddled with guilt for not spending those extra minutes with Sarah.

"Are you mad at me?" I asked Sarah the next morning. We were sitting inside Bruegger's, the aroma of yeast wafting through the space. Students and locals stood in line buying hot coffees and warm bagels.

"No, Blu. I could never be mad at you. Disappointed, that's all."

"Welcome to my world." I wrapped up the remainder of my honey grain bagel, too sad to eat.

"This is hard for me too. Linda has stopped bringing up your name, but I sense she still feels threatened by you, scared I'm going to kick her out. The thing is, even while I'm telling her you're just a friend, in the back of my mind I'm contemplating telling her the truth. I just don't have a clue how that would work for us." Sarah patted her eyes with a tissue. "Just know I love you."

I'd always thought "I love you" held so much weight, but words, I'd learned, were cheap. Actions were where the money was. And Sarah's actions—holding me in her arms, yet keeping me at arm's length—was telling. I can only guess that she was torn with doing what was right (staying with Linda and not upsetting their home life) and doing what felt right (being with me and throwing all of what she had away.) I was too young to see that perhaps Sarah was just selfish and liked having Linda take care of everything, and liked having me to satisfy her other needs.

I stared out the front window. People in colorful winter jackets trudged along Pleasant Street, smiling up at the bright sunlight, seemingly without a care in the world, while my heart was being pummeled. Our relationship was a constant push-pull of emotions—wanting to be together, yet knowing it wasn't possible—and neither of us willing to stop it. What's worse, I'd begun dreaming of a life with Sarah. Of living together, preparing dinners, and falling asleep each night in her arms. As happy as those dreams made me, reality was never far behind. I'd become less concerned with the lesbian label, thanks to the conversation with Dad, but the May-December stamp of approval seemed a harder one to obtain. I had no female role models to compare us to, no one to assure me that what we were doing was normal or, at the very least, not abnormal. Sure, there was Mark and his older boyfriend, but gay men seemed a whole other species. I'd finally fallen in love. Finally met someone I wanted to bring home for Thanksgiving, take as my plus one to weddings. I should've felt elated. Instead, my apprehension of what everyone would think kept me feeling ashamed.

Decisions, Decisions
January 1994–May 1994

Nana B. and I reclined on lounge chairs at her Delray Beach community pool. Toddlers splashed in the shallow end, teenagers swam in the deep end, and grandparents walked back and forth in the middle, wearing wide-brimmed hats and oversized sunglasses.

I'd been in Florida a week and had slipped right into our annual routine: mornings playing Rummikub while her friends, "the girls," called, asking of our plans, which included the pool, flea markets, and early bird dinners. Every minute spent with Nana B. and the girls distracted me from Sarah. As did those afternoons with my other grandparents (who lived nearby in Boca Raton), listening to Papa tell me more stories about the war.

One night, we were watching *Jeopardy*—Nana B. crocheting an afghan, and me beside her untangling yarn—when her phone rang. Nana B. chatted with the caller, then handed me the phone and whispered, "Your boss. When did you get a job?"

I shrugged as I put the phone to my head. "Hello?"

"Blu!" Sarah exclaimed. "I have incredible news."

"You got a gig as a lounge singer?" I walked down the hallway, past dozens of hanging photos of me and my cousins from my dad's side of the family.

"Admissions needs someone to rewrite the major sheets for

prospective students. I offered to help pay for this person if they'd also work as the night director next summer. I even said they could work at the desk in my office."

"You'd risk a stranger in your office?" In the kitchen I removed a homemade oatmeal-raisin cookie from a ceramic jar Nana B. had painted.

"Not a stranger. You. I mentioned you were looking for a job. The director knows you're great from when you were the green dean. She's familiar with the column you used to write for the *Collegian*. And with my recommendation. . ." Sarah paused. "It's only thirty hours a week, plus benefits. You'll have time for your writing, and we'd get to see each other every day."

"But what if I get a writing job in New York City?" No offer had been made, but Ben had said his editor had been impressed with the pieces I'd submitted.

"Blu, until you've got a full-time column gig or an offer from a book publisher, you might as well have a steady paycheck and benefits."

I took another cookie. "What happens when orientations end?"

"I'm creating a position in my office. They've been pushing me to get an in-house designer for all our publications."

"I've never designed publications."

"You're artistic and a quick learner."

Excited as I was at the prospect of being back in Amherst, I wondered how complicated it might get dealing with Linda. Not to mention Rachel judging us. "I appreciate the offer, but can I think about it?"

"What's there to think about, Blu?"

I hung up and called my uncle.

"Let me play devil's advocate," Mark said. "You haven't applied for other jobs. Why not look elsewhere?"

"Because I know I'll like this job. Plus, I could go to grad school for free. After six months as a part-time employee, I'd get tuition reimbursement."

"Felice," his voice grew serious. "Sarah might've gotten you the job, but it doesn't mean you owe her anything."

~

January 11, 1994

Dear Sarah,

Having a purpose has me feeling like my old self again: energized and excited! I've learned so much these last few months, mostly how it feels to be in love. Would this have happened without Warm Tuna? God bless Chicken of the Sea. ♥Blu

P.S. Our horoscope today: "Cancer: You'll have a relationship with your boss." How'd they know?

January 14, 1994

Blu,

It's a whole new day and a whole new world for us! I've got a shit-eating grin thinking of you happy to have a purpose again. I know you have trepidations about coming back and how that will work. I've got them too. But I know that being able to be close to you and see your smile and even just occasionally touch you makes my life brighter and better. I also know that even though every molecule of me wants to spend as much time with you as there is to spend, that's not realistic. I know you'll have a life outside of work, and I just want to be a part of some of it, however much you say. We know Linda bowls on Saturdays, but if you have something else scheduled for Saturday, it will be OK. I can't control your life. Also know that anytime you want to be with me I'll do anything I can to arrange it—that's how I've been operating since September so it's just natural. Please know that this secret relationship is not easy for me either. I realize for you it is tough not to be able to be open and obvious about your feelings when it is so much a part of your primary emotional life. That's one of the most common problems of this not-so-easy life preference. But the nature of us makes it even more difficult. Okay, so it doesn't make sense—but it does—why else would it have happened against all odds? Guess the conscious decision for me was just to go with what I was feeling and not anguish and try to attack it intellectually or even rationally for fear it would somehow disappear in words and negatives and that's the last thing I want to happen. There is more to say on this—your thoughts and feelings—and I want to hear it because it's important and we need to share it and understand each other. Just know that whatever will make life happier for you—and it's

> within my power—I'll do because I love you. Can't wait to spend my Saturdays with you. WOFTOG! S.
>
> P.S. Our horoscope today: "Cancer: The way you handle office pressures and interruptions determines how fast you move up the corporate ladder." What type of interruptions? Looking forward to finding out.

"Surprise!" My family wore UMass sweatshirts (courtesy of Alumni Affairs) as they greeted me in the kitchen on my last morning waking up with a Cape Cod address. I was excited but sad; our tight-knit family was splitting apart.

"No crying." Meredith spied my tears as she handed me a crayon drawing of our family for the fridge in my new apartment.

"See you next week when you help me organize my new dorm." Jackie hugged me, then headed upstairs to go back to sleep.

Dad and I, wearing layers of winter gear, fit my futon, a small couch, and a disassembled shelf unit inside the family caravan. We packed my computer, clothes, toiletries, and kitchen items into my car's back seat, which Dad then rearranged to make sure I could see out the rearview mirror.

Mom came outside wearing a winter coat and handed me a bag of apples and a jar of honey. "This is an important time for you sweetheart. Spend it reflecting on what you enjoyed growing up, so you'll recognize what to hold on to as you begin this next phase of your life. May your new home be as sweet as this one."

"Thanks."

"You know my wish is for you to be happy, but could you do me one favor?" Mom and I hadn't talked since my disclosure to Dad, but I knew he'd told her. Her cheeks, crimson from the cold, pulled back into a smile. "Promise me you'll find yourself a nice Jewish girl." A joke, yes, but a kind gesture. My parents supported me; I'd never doubted it. But they only knew part one of the story. Sarah was part two. And it was the red flags of part two—large age difference and Linda—that kept me from giving them the option of sharing in my happiness.

It's obvious now, but my hesitation to face what I was doing didn't really concern how I'd look in their eyes, but how I'd look in my own.

~

"Welcome to your palace." Sarah gave me a pro forma hug when Dad and I arrived in Amherst that afternoon. Feeling her body against mine sent my libido into overdrive.

I'd agreed to a one-year lease of the one-bedroom apartment at the Colonial Village complex, trusting Sarah's opinion and description when she'd checked it out the week before.

"This place gets good light." I stood by the living room window, which faced the parking lot and a small yard covered in snow.

"And plenty of closets for you to organize," added Sarah.

"And electric heat." Dad lifted his glasses to examine the thermostat. "You realize what that means?"

"Yes." I rolled my eyes. "Wear lots of sweaters." I knew not having roommates would be more expensive but having a place of my own seemed worth it. Sarah had agreed, adding, "There comes a time when a woman needs her own bathroom."

"Phone and cable are installed," Sarah said. "And your first month's on me. Your housewarming gift."

"Really? Thank you."

It took us an hour to carry everything inside. At one point, when Dad used the bathroom, Sarah and I snuck a kiss. Then she left, and Dad and I began assembling shelves.

"Sarah's a good friend." He held two planks in place while I screwed them together. "Does she have a partner?"

"Yes. They've been together thirteen years."

"Any kids?"

"Five."

"Five kids?" He sounded shocked.

"Well, they're cats, but don't tell her that."

After dinner at Judie's (Dad loved their popovers too), we went to a men's basketball game. My former boss Bonnie in the basketball office had gotten us tickets.

Back at my apartment, Dad slept on my futon while I slept on the couch, both of us keeping on our winter hats.

"You lose ninety percent of your body heat through your head," Dad reminded me for the hundredth time since I was seven.

~

Before he left the next morning, Dad said, "Drive safely on these snowy roads and change the oil in your car every three thousand miles," which I interpreted as, "I love you. Take care of yourself."

Once alone in my apartment, surrounded by bags of stuff, I put on a Guns N' Roses CD and unpacked every box. I wanted to wake up the next day prepared to start my new life.

Mid-morning, Sarah called. "How's the unpacking going, Blu?"

"Great, but how are you able to call me on a Sunday?" I was under my desk, connecting computer cables.

"There's a pay phone at the deli where I pick up the *Times.* I wanted to tell you I plan to be at your place early tomorrow because they said we're expecting another storm."

"Who's they?" I teased.

That night I dreamt I was hosting a party in my new apartment. Through the window was a magnificent view of the Manhattan skyline. It was raining outside and every time another friend arrived, my apartment got larger, like a mushroom after a rain.

"I'm so glad you're back, Blu." Sarah had let herself in with her own key the next morning and joined me under two comforters.

"Me too." I rubbed my hands along her back to warm her and was startled by the delicateness of her spine. I didn't remember her being so fragile. "I can't wait to go to movies at Pleasant Street, see concerts at the Iron Horse, and—"

"With me?" Sarah asked.

"Yes, with you."

"But you don't say that."

"I don't say that because I assume you won't be able to go because you'll have plans with Linda." I knew there would always be more give than take.

"We've been over this, Blu." Sarah's face was inches from mine, her expression pained. "Linda's not thrilled you're back, and I'm trying to keep a happy balance."

"Do you love Linda more than me?"

"You've got to stop asking that. You know you've captured my heart." Sarah kissed the tip of my nose. "Now come on, we should be celebrating. Today's the first of our many days together."

"Yeah, as long as Linda has bowling or golf."

"Please can we try to enjoy the time we have together?" Sarah's blue eyes canceled my frustration and we picked up where we'd left off in Provincetown. Heavy discussion shelved once again.

We spent the Martin Luther King holiday sealing windows and hanging pictures. It snowed, and I wished for road closures so Sarah would have to spend the night.

"I think we should name your apartment Milford," Sarah suggested over dinner. "It makes me think of that wonderful afternoon we shared there."

"Milford it is!"

We put on the news. There'd been an earthquake in Los Angeles and at least fifty people had died. As gripped as we were by the tragedy, it didn't stop us from moving into the bedroom for round two.

"This is my favorite place to be," I whispered in the dark.

"In your apartment?"

"No, silly. In your arms."

A few moments later, Sarah slipped out of bed.

"Are you leaving?" I asked.

"You know I have to go." Sarah dressed in the dark. "But at least we have an entire season ahead of us."

Yeah, an entire season of her leaving me.

The front door closed with a convincing thud. A wrenching gripped my stomach. Had moving back been a mistake? That's when I heard the door reopen.

"There's at least a foot of snow out there," Sarah said. "Even I'm not dumb enough to drive in this." She called Linda, explained the situation, and got back in bed. With Sarah's arms around me, I was sure that moving back had been the right decision.

"Delayed opening." I repeated the university's hotline message the next morning. Overnight the snow had turned to ice. We could stay in bed longer. And we did.

We drove to work in Sarah's car, the sky a crystal blue. After stopping for bagels, I said I'd walk to the office. Sarah thought I was being ridiculous, but the repercussions of us arriving together on my first day scared me more than slipping on ice.

By the time I'd trudged up the walkway to admissions, the three-story modern building with an all-glass entrance once home to a fraternity, it hit me: I might've been armed with a job, health benefits, and the beginnings of a retirement plan, but I was still closer to middle school than middle age. Didn't matter though, adulthood was knocking at my door. Literally.

A persistent patter caused me to look up. Sarah was waving down to me from her office window. I waved back, wondering if getting me this job had been more about giving Sarah a purpose than giving me one.

I entered the building and headed up the stairwell.

"I heard you'd be working here." Kimberly's cheery demeanor caught me off guard. The last time I'd seen her was three months earlier, when she'd given me the cold shoulder at the Saturday info session. I knew the chances of seeing her in the building were high, since she was a tour guide, but on my first day? "I'm glad I bumped into you. I wanted to be the one to tell you. I'm seeing someone. She goes to Smith."

My first instinct? To say I was also seeing someone. Not for competitive reasons, but because I wanted to share that news.

"That's great." I removed my hat.

"I love your haircut. Guess you decided."

"What do you mean?" I smoothed down my hair, assuming my wool hat had messed it.

She smirked. "You know, short hair. Lesbian."

Would that word ever stop making me uncomfortable? We continued in opposite directions, promising to get together soon.

Sarah was waiting for me when I exited the stairwell on the third floor. "I'm here to escort you to your new office, ma'am."

"Who are you calling a ma'am?" I followed her down the hall to what we'd no longer refer to as Sarah's office, but our office. On my desk was a copy of that day's *Collegian* opened to the personals, a heart drawn in red ink around one: "Blu. Welcome Home. Now I believe miracles can happen. S."

The sound of the door closing made me pivot. Sarah wore a "we did it!" expression as she turned the lock. In her embrace, I caught my reflection in the window. The bars of the fire escape outside made me look trapped inside a cage.

"Since you enjoy challenges." Sarah reopened the door and sat at her customary seat at the "head" of her round table. "I've come up with one for us." She held up a blue map of the UMass campus, the same one we put in the new students' orientation packet. "This will be our kissing map. Our goal is to kiss in every building and mark it on the map."

"Are you nuts? What if someone heard you?" I glanced at the door, expecting someone to be standing there, mouth agape.

"Blu, stop worrying." Sarah removed the cap from a yellow highlighter. "Did we kiss in the Student Union?"

"No, but we did in the parking garage."

Sarah's expression brightened as she colored over the garage square. Then she walked over to the door, brushed aside a navy blazer hanging on the back she kept for unexpected meetings, and taped up our kissing map.

Game on.

The morning of our first Saturday, Sarah and I met at the Black Sheep Bakery. I'd walked, since it had snowed, and the roads were slick. Ever since I'd totaled my car in a blizzard the year before, the visual still fresh in my mind—blinding snow, tires sliding, my car smashing into a truck and skidding off the highway, the whole incident lasting seconds—if one flake came down, I didn't get behind the wheel. In fact, I took the bus to work every day that first week because of snow. Sarah drove me home after work, and sometimes we'd go on errands for a soap dish or ice cube trays. Sarah also brought me items from her house she said they no longer wanted: area rugs, serving bowls, vases. I wondered if Linda had any suspicion those items were now sprucing up my place.

While Sarah paid for our sandwiches, I ripped a tab off a flier on the community bulletin board, excited to find a posting for an eight-week creative writing class.

We took the sandwiches in to see *Schindler's List*. The irony of sneaking food into a Holocaust movie was not lost on me. The film left me thinking of my grandfather, so we sat in the food court, and I wrote down my thoughts. Sarah, across from me, her foot on mine under the table, read the *Times Book Review*. When I suggested we get our pictures taken in the photo booth at the arcade, Sarah loved the idea.

Back at Milford, it was back to watching the clock, so we got back into bed. Not long after, Sarah got up.

"Are you going to the bathroom?" I asked. "Or leaving?"

"It's eight, Blu. That's the deal. I have to get home before Linda."

"Five more minutes? Please?"

Sarah kneeled on the futon and pressed her hand over my heart. "Remember, even when I'm not here, I'm still there."

Once alone, I asked the empty room, "Where is 'still there?'" More importantly, why was I? Because I loved her and figured this was the price I had to pay.

"The director ordered another twelve neckties," I told Rachel when I stopped by her office.

"This could prove to be an actual business for you." She was holding one of several maroon UMass golf-towel samples spread out on her desk.

"You sound like my father." I sat on the rocking chair as the radiator in the corner hissed. "He thinks anything I do well is a potential business venture."

"He knows you're capable of a lot. Speaking of which, want to play on my UMass coed softball team? Season starts mid-April."

"Sure. Thanks."

"So." Rachel tossed the towel onto the desk. "Now that you've been back a few weeks, how are things?"

"You mean how are things with Sarah?"

She nodded. "I only ask because I care about you both."

"Things are great. Besides work, we spend Saturdays together."

"As long as you're happy."

I rocked back. "I am." At least I was when I was with Sarah. The rest of the time was another story, but Rachel was the last person I would admit that to.

My writing class was in a second-floor apartment inside of a large Victorian in Northampton. There were six of us, all women, spread out on mismatched furniture in the cozy living room.

Olivia, the instructor and an assistant professor at Smith College, had skin the color of umber, wore thick bunchy socks, and had been leading these classes for almost a decade.

"Your writing warmup," Olivia said, "is to finish this sentence: I write because. . ." Pens began scratching against paper. I looked down at my blank notebook and wrote: "I write because I don't have a choice. I feel controlled by it. If something happens in my life, I have the need to record it. A kind of therapy. I carry paper and a pen wherever I go."

"I want money, lots and lots of money!"

I reached an arm out from beneath my two comforters to turn up my radio alarm clock's volume. "I Wanna Be Rich" by Calloway had been a favorite song in college. Energized, I jumped out of bed, made it, put on two sweatshirts, then started a load of laundry. I couldn't write until I completed little chores, which motivated me toward the larger one.

"I want the pie in the sky!"

Now when I thought of money, it was as a test of my values, since I paid the bills, and any unnecessary expenditure violated those newer values, such as not getting frostbite in my own apartment. Sarah paid for activities when we went out, but she also paid for Linda, since Linda was her "wife." Would I have rather been the wife than the mistress? Part of me did. Part of me wanted that security. Not for financial reasons, but to have someone beside me, supporting me. With Sarah I felt loved, stable, and secure. She buoyed my confidence, making me think I could take on the world.

Bundled up in hats and scarves, Sarah and I left the office at noon and walked along the plowed pathways where students plodded along in snow boots, hunched over from heavy backpacks, as flakes fluttered around us.

We bought bowls of chili and brown rice from Earthfoods, a cafe in the Student Union, and ate inside the Cape Cod Lounge. Seated on an orange couch, we looked out soaring windows that faced Machmer Hall.

"It was right there." Sarah pointed out the window. "Where

students picketed in support of Bobby Seale and the Black Panthers in 1970."

We left, and I showed Sarah an underground passageway to the Campus Center I'd used when I'd been a DJ and carted record albums from the Hillel office to the radio station. Sarah was thrilled because it provided a "romantic" space to sneak a kiss.

Walking back to the office we stopped inside Hasbrouck Laboratory and found an empty classroom.

"Two more buildings to highlight!" Sarah exclaimed, eager to update our kissing map.

"Do you know what time it is?" Sarah asked later that afternoon when she turned on the radio. Terry Gross was introducing *Fresh Air* on NPR.

"Four o'clock," I said without looking at my watch. I remembered hearing Gross's distinctive voice in the background during our late-afternoon phone calls last fall.

"Right. And do you know what that means?"

"One hour until the chains come off?" My eyes remained on the computer screen. I was creating a brochure for parents of new students. A work-study student had been teaching me a design program, and I took to it right away. Putting text and images together was no different from assembling a jigsaw puzzle.

"No, smartass." Sarah locked the door. "Our time." She stepped over to the window. "Come here, Blu."

I got up and walked over. From behind me, Sarah clasped her arms around my waist and kissed my neck as I stared out across campus. Were other staffers doing what we were doing behind their closed office doors?

"Isn't the snow pretty?" Sarah said. Snowflakes were whitening trees, rooftops, and cars. Amherst had a historic number of snowstorms that winter.

"Yes, as long as I don't have to drive in it." I whirled around. "Can you come over tonight? You can say you're watching the game at Rafters with work friends." I'd been coming up with excuses for Sarah to spend time with me, and thanks in part to a lanky recruit named Marcus Camby, the men's basketball team was having a remarkable season, giving us an effortless explanation.

"I can't. Linda and I are having dinner with—"

I stopped listening. When Sarah talked of her public life, I second-guessed warm tuna, second-guessed moving back to Amherst, and second-guessed what I was doing. What confused me was my skin still tingled from her slightest touch.

"We could have appetizers here, though." Sarah lowered me to the floor. How strange to be lying on the floor of the office I'd once felt too intimidated to enter, beneath the woman who'd intimidated me, her weight forcing the scratchy industrial carpet into my back as our bodies writhed. By the time Terry Gross thanked her guest, we were pulling up our pants.

"Are you sure you can't come over?" I asked.

"I have dinner plans." Sarah drew a comb through her hair.

"You always have dinner plans. Can't you get out of it this once? Or is it that you'd rather spend your time with Linda?" I put on my wool hat. No comb could hide this evidence.

"Blu, you know the drill."

I knew it too well. I had become an expert at accepting whatever I could get. I might not have had Sarah all the time, but I had her love, and for the moment, that was enough.

"You're not even coming in?" I said when Sarah pulled up to my apartment fifteen minutes later and left the car running. "Even for a minute?"

"I want to, but Linda's waiting."

"Linda's always waiting." I pulled the handle and pushed hard. The car door flew open. Snowflakes whooshed in.

"Blu, you know I'm still there."

Still where?

"Please come in," I begged.

"I have to go." Sarah kissed me passionately, but rushed. Always rushed.

Seconds after entering my apartment, there was a knock. Had Sarah changed her mind? Was it snowing too hard?

"Hi," said a woman with long, dark hair spilling out of a fleece winter hat. She was a few inches taller than I was, and her posture made me self-consciously stand up straighter. "I'm Allison. I just moved in and need help carrying my TV inside. Would you mind?"

I introduced myself as I followed her to the parking lot.

"Are you the Felice from the *Collegian*?" Allison hopped up into the bed of her pickup truck. I nodded. "I loved your column. I had a friend who wrote for the paper." She slid the television, wrapped in a garbage bag, to the edge. "Her name was Heather. Did you know her?"

Was asking if you knew a gay person a telltale sign that the asker was gay?

"Yes." I wiped flakes from my cheeks. "How did you know her?"

"She dated one of my teammates."

That's when I recognized her. "Are you Allison the All-American?" It had been a tagline on the *Collegian's* sports page for weeks my junior year. I pictured her long muscular leg extended after a kick, face stern, ponytail swaying. "The sports editor said you were the best soccer player ever to play for UMass."

"I wouldn't say the best." But the gleam in her eyes said she was happy to be recognized.

"I don't know how you did it. Division I is your whole life. UMass recruited me to play volleyball and softball, but I quit both, since there wasn't a future for me playing sports."

"I get it," Allison said as we walked to her apartment, the unwieldy TV between us. "But it's what I want to do. I'm getting my master's in exercise science and am an assistant coach on the team."

We placed the television on her living room floor near a mesh bag full of soccer balls and a stack of unopened boxes.

"I'm meeting friends tonight at the North Star," Allison said. "Want to come?"

I was about to say no, then thought of Sarah out living her public life.

The North Star was several steps up from Our Hideaway. For starters, it wasn't hidden in the backwoods, but was a block from downtown Northampton. It also had disco lights and a much better sound system. Melissa Etheridge's voice pulsed in my ears as we maneuvered through the dense crowd of women our age. I kept my eyes peeled for anyone I might recognize, unsure whether I'd say hello or try to disappear. I spotted Kimberly at the pool table with her arm around a woman her same height, wearing a backwards baseball cap and Boston Bruins jersey. Kimberly saw me and gave me the thumbs up. She was the only one who knew how much it had taken for me to enter the place.

Allison and I joined her friends, all former and current UMass athletes, seated around a few small tables, their faces bathed in flashing colored lights. They were toasting one of the women who'd just been chosen as the next goalie on the United States women's national soccer team.

"How do you know Allison?" asked a softball pitcher, whose shirt sleeve was so tight around her defined bicep it resembled a sausage casing.

"We're neighbors," I said.

"My girlfriend and I are throwing a birthday party for our dog. You should come with Allison."

"Thanks." Excitement built at the possibility of having a life outside Sarah. Maybe warm tuna could work. "When is it?"

"Saturday," she said. My enthusiasm faded.

The morning sky was a sheet of thick, ominous clouds. Forecasters called for the next snowstorm to begin around noon, making the preceding night's snowfall just a preview. From my apartment, I watched the PVTA bus pull into the complex and brush against the piles of plowed dirty snow. I'd planned to take the bus to work, but Sarah had insisted on picking me up, saying, "Gives us a little morning time together." Not the morning time I preferred, but beggars can't be choosers.

When her car appeared, I ran outside.

"Seeing your smile is my favorite moment of the day." Sarah leaned over the gear shift and kissed me. As she pulled onto Route 9, I told her about Allison, the North Star, and being invited to a birthday party for a dog.

"But Saturday's our day." Sarah glanced at me.

"I know. I said I had plans."

Sarah pulled up to the admissions building. "I have a meeting with the chancellor and should be back around noon. Lunch at

Milford?"

"Sure." I stepped out of the car as new snowflakes fell.

Later that morning, Peg poked her head into our office to say the university was closing early and she was heading home. "Need a ride, or will Sarah take you?"

"Sarah may have gone home already," I said, knowing Sarah would never leave without telling me. Since my return, I was sure Peg knew what was going on with us. A few times she had walked into our office when Sarah was standing behind my chair rubbing my neck. I had worried about Peg, but Sarah assured me Peg was loyal. Sometimes I wondered if Sarah had wanted to get caught. It would've removed the burden of juggling two lives, not to mention lying all the time. Plus, it would've also saved Sarah from having to do the adult thing and tell Linda the truth.

By noon, everyone had left work. I took advantage of the quiet and finished rewriting more major sheets for admissions.

"Students are planning to take over our building!" said a shaky voice. "You and I are the only ones here." The admissions director stood in our office doorway in her signature high heels and short skirt, her normally taut bun loose with flyaway strands curled around her head. An authoritative presence on most days, she now looked as frazzled as she sounded. "We've got to lock all the doors."

Loud voices were coming from outside. I leapt to the window. Through thick white flakes, I made out a massive group of students walking up the path, holding signs and chanting, "Hey, hey! Ho, ho! Tuition hikes have got to go!"

"They're here," I said. The director bolted. I began locking doors on the third floor when the stairwell door burst open and a student wearing a UMass ski hat flew out and almost knocked me down.

"Sorry!" he yelled over his shoulder as he raced down the hall, his boots leaving water stains on the carpet. Other students poured out of the stairwell.

I hurried down to the main floor and found students seated in offices, talking on phones, and making posters.

"Did you hear the good news?" a female student asked me,

assuming I was part of the takeover. Because of the weather, I was dressed in jeans and a UMass sweatshirt. "We found a master key and have access to all the offices."

I sprinted back up the stairs. Our office door was open and a male student was seated in Sarah's chair, her phone to his ear. He nodded at me and spoke into the phone, "Hey. We've taken over the admissions building. Come, we'll be here all night."

Another male student strumming a guitar strolled by. My new office mate walked out, and I picked up my phone.

"*Daily Collegian*," answered a familiar voice.

"Cindy? Hi, it's Felice."

"Sorry, I can't talk. There's this student takeover and—"

"I know," I whispered to the newest editor-in-chief. "I'm in admissions."

"You are?"

"I work here now." I told her my idea for writing about the takeover from an undercover perspective, a Nellie Bly insider's take.

"Love it," she said. "Get me five hundred words by tonight."

I began jotting down notes about how I felt hearing the students' shouts and seeing them inside offices, feeling like there was a party going on at my parents' house that was out of my control, when a tap on the window caught my attention. Sarah was standing on the fire escape, flakes falling around her as if she were inside a snow globe.

I darted into the hall and opened the emergency door. Sarah stomped her boots, and snow fell off in clumps. She walked toward our office, but a hefty male student blocked her, his bulk filling the doorway.

"Move out of her way," said a man's voice from up the hall. We turned to see Tim, the orientation counselor from last summer whose lack of clean clothes had inspired the Bathrobe Tour. As student government president, he oversaw the takeover.

"Thanks," Sarah said when the Hulk-double stepped aside.

"I owed you," said Tim.

Sarah stuffed a few folders into her briefcase, since we didn't know how long this interruption would last. I grabbed my backpack, and we left, walking arm in arm down the slippery fire escape.

"What do you say we pick up slices from Antonio's and head to Milford?" Sarah inched slowly out of the parking lot.

"To eat or can you stay over?"

"Stay over. The roads are icy, and every Girl Scout knows safety first."

At my apartment, I began typing the takeover story. Sarah called Linda to say that sleet was covering the snow and that she was at my place. My fingers froze above the keyboard.

When Sarah hung up, I asked, "Why did you tell Linda you were here?"

"I figured the truth was less conspicuous."

"Is she upset?"

"She's not thrilled, but she's glad I'm not driving in this." Sarah kissed me. All parts of my body responded, but I resisted.

"As much as I love that you get to sleep over, it's only because there's a snowstorm, not because you chose to." I folded my arms like a pouty toddler.

Sarah crouched down and rested her palms on my lap. "I thought this is what you wanted, Blu. You have your space, and you also have me."

"I only have you at work and on Saturdays. It's not enough."

"Am I making you more unhappy than happy?"

"Sometimes. Like when I want to call you and say goodnight."

"I'm here now." Sarah brushed her fingers across my cheek.

"But this is a fluke."

"Blu, listen to me. I'd love to be with you all the time, but you wouldn't want that. Despite what you think, we have the perfect relationship. We don't live together."

Was she serious? Did not living with someone make a relationship perfect? My parents had lived together a quarter of a century and their relationship seemed close to perfect. Maybe it was different with lesbians. Maybe living apart avoided lesbian bed death. Sarah was the experienced one, so I deferred to her.

Two hours later, satisfied with diction, style, and length, I climbed into bed and rested my head on Sarah's shoulder. She put down her book and wrapped her arms around me. Still charged from the events of the day, I watched snow collect outside the window, feeling content in her embrace, knowing she would stay all night. It again made me question her theory that living apart made a relationship perfect. This glimpse of what it would be like if we did live together didn't seem so bad to me.

The takeover didn't last through the weekend. The snowstorm hampered the students' objective, but not ours. Despite my initial petulance, that unexpected overnight with Sarah put a permanent smile on my face.

"I got you extra copies to send to your Florida fan club." Sarah nodded to the stack of *Collegians* on my desk when I arrived at work Monday morning. "I'd love to take you to dinner tonight to celebrate Valentine's Day, but Linda made plans for us and—"

"Whatever, no worries." I was in too good a mood to allow Sarah's public life to spoil it. And on Valentine's Day of all days.

Work flew as people called, emailed, or stopped by to congratulate me. It had been a long time since my last published column in the *Collegian*, whose circulation was in the thousands (the *Cape Cod Sports Report's,* with a much smaller distribution, didn't count), and it increased my appetite big time.

At noon, Sarah and I hit Milford for "lunch." Before we left, she handed me an envelope.

"Plane tickets to Tahiti?" I ripped open the envelope. Sarah was always joking about us running off there. Inside was a hand-drawn coupon for six golf lessons at Holyoke Community College.

"Thought it would be helpful to get a few pointers, so we'll be ready to hit the links once spring arrives," Sarah said. "Plus, it's a great excuse to spend one night a week together."

Sarah was trying to make me happy. Finding another reason for us to spend time together succeeded at this. I never thought she was trying to keep me caught up in what we had, which is to say, keeping me accepting a little in lieu of nothing. Sarah had been upfront from the start about never kicking Linda out, meaning we could never be together. I'd gone along with it, believing she was trying to please everyone, and this was the only way she knew how. Perhaps I was a touch naïve. Despite her selfish and manipulative behaviors, my feelings for her didn't diminish, though my love was starting to become tarnished.

~

"A toast to you on your published column." Allison raised her wine glass. We were seated at a table for two in Pizzeria Paradiso. The Northampton restaurant was bustling with waiters carrying plates of pasta and carafes of wine in between busboys delivering baskets of gorgonzola bread. As we clinked glasses, Sarah appeared and introduced herself to Allison as my boss.

"Mind if I borrow Felice for a minute?" Sarah said. "Work question."

I followed Sarah to the bar, where couples waited to be seated.

"Who's that woman you're with?" Sarah's voice was neutral.

"That's Allison, my neighbor." I glanced over. Allison had been watching us and looked away.

"Is there anything else you'd care to tell me about her? You're out to dinner on Valentine's Day."

"So are you. But unlike you, I won't be sleeping with anyone tonight."

The bartender, a slender guy wearing a thin black tie, winked at me as he slid two tumblers across the bar to an older gentleman. Did he think I was having an argument with my mother?

"I've told you. Linda and I haven't been sexual in years. Last fall, she sensed me pulling away and tried to rekindle the flame, but I couldn't cheat on you. You're the one I'm in love with."

There it was: the dyke drama Heather had warned me about. But she'd never warned me the drama itself could become something I'd crave.

"Shouldn't you tell that to Linda so she can find someone who is in love with her?" It was easy to put the blame on Sarah, telling her she should be honest, but I was being just as dishonest by not stopping her actions.

Sarah's body deflated, her rigid back replaced by a curved resignation. "I'm sorry, Blu. I was jealous seeing you with someone. Let me make it up to you."

"How?"

She plucked a box of matches from a bowl on the bar. "Come line dancing with me Wednesday night at the North Star. The couple we're with tonight invited me, since Linda has a dinner with her bowling friends."

"Won't your friends tell Linda?"

Sarah shook her head. "You can meet me. I'll say I bumped into you like I did tonight."

I agreed because that's how our relationship worked: every moment together pre-planned with a lie.

"I'm twenty-three, and I won a gold medal at the Olympics," said a US skier. I had the *Today* show on as I got ready for work. I too was twenty-three, though I'd never won anything nearly as amazing as an Olympic medal. But I had a choice. Either I let that depress me, or I used it as motivation to achieve my goals, which at that point included writing my grandfather's story. This was a sizable goal, however. How did one even go about achieving it? Then I remembered Dad's suggestion of creating a syllabus and breaking my goal into steps, the same way I might organize a closet: first go through shirts, then pants, then shoes. I vowed to stop getting caught up in what I hadn't done and to focus on what I could do.

"Turn with your left! Step forward! That's it!" The line-dancing instructor, a burly man in tight jeans, denim shirt, and turquoise bolo tie, stomped in time to the music. Men and women in cowboy boots stepped back and forth in parallel rows on the dance floor. The median age that night at the North Star was double, if not triple, the typical Friday-night regulars, making me feel as though I'd stepped into an episode of *The Twilight Zone*, in which everyone had aged overnight.

"What a surprise to see you." Sarah remained seated when I approached her table. She introduced me to her two friends, attorneys who each had short salt-and-pepper hair and wore matching crewneck wool sweaters in different colors. "Ladies, this is Felice. She's a budding writer who works in my office."

They said hello then continued their conversation about retirement funds and wills, topics I found uninteresting.

"We're starting a new dance," the instructor announced. "Everyone come on out!"

"Are you coming?" I was half out of my seat.

"Oh, no," Sarah said. "You go. Have fun."

Was she not going to dance after inviting me?

I danced for a few songs until they slowed down the music. A woman in a leopard-print vest asked me to dance. I debated saying yes, thinking it might make Sarah jealous, but Sarah was locked in conversation and probably wouldn't even have noticed. I apologized to the woman and charged back to the table.

"The house is in my name, and my will states—" Sarah stopped speaking when I dug my fingers into her clavicle.

"Sorry to interrupt." I put on a fake smile. "Wanted to say good night. Need to get up early for work. Can't be late or the boss might fire me. Nice meeting you."

Outside it was drizzling and cold. I flipped up my hood and headed down the sidewalk.

"Blu, why are you leaving?" Sarah caught up to me near a row of parked cars. I stopped under a streetlight, water droplets glistening on their way down.

"Because you ignored me. Why'd you even invite me?"

"Because I want to spend time with you every chance I get." Sarah stepped closer as though to hug me, then stepped back realizing she couldn't. Anyone watching would think she were line dancing. "You know I can't be who you want me to be in public."

"Yes, because you've got to protect Linda. I'm tired of hiding. If you really loved me, then…" As usual I stopped, unable to finish that sentence, as raindrops mixed with tears on my cheeks.

A week later, Sarah arrived at work announcing that Dinah Shore, the television personality and supporter of women's golf, had died.

"That's too bad." I was sitting at the computer, pasting images into a housing-options handout. "Today's my mom's birthday. She's forty-seven."

"She's a looker, your mother. And the apple doesn't fall too far from the tree. How's your mom taking being almost fifty?"

"She sounded freaked out when I called her this morning. I reminded her age is only an issue when you can no longer control your bladder."

"True." Sarah sifted through a stack of letters Peg had left on her desk for her to sign. "But in our society, age is measured in beauty, particularly for women."

I lifted my arms and stretched back. "Why are gray-haired older men considered distinguished, while women with the same features are old maids?"

"It doesn't matter to you, right?" Sarah looked at me as if in need of assurance.

I nodded, though inside I wasn't sure. Sarah was almost sixty. To people my age that was old. And though I didn't see Sarah as old, I was aware of our age difference. For instance, when she said things like, "The apple doesn't fall too far from the tree." Or when I first noticed her radio channels were pre-programmed to NPR. My awareness of our age difference, coupled with my constant concern for what people would think if they found out about us, added to my simmering unease. And when uncertainty flooded my mind, I did what I always did: reminded myself we were a secret and there was no point concerning myself with something that wasn't going anywhere.

Jackie typed a history paper on my computer while I sat on my couch editing a writing class assignment about my grandfather's experience in the Bergen Belsen concentration camp.

At noon my parents and Meredith arrived. This would be my first Saturday away from Sarah in two months. My family and I spent the afternoon walking in and out of stores in Northampton, happy to find the early March weather considerably warmer. Inside a fine arts gallery, my parents bought new wedding rings to celebrate their anniversary. That night they stayed at the Lord Jeffrey Inn, and my sisters slept at my place. The three of us stayed up late playing Boggle and eating brownies made from a mix.

The next morning, Mom and Dad arrived with warm bagels. As Mom and I cut up fruit in the kitchen, she asked if I was okay, saying I looked like I'd lost weight. I told her I'd had a bug, but was fine. I hated to lie, but how could I tell her the cause of my stomach ailment was a secret love affair?

Mid-afternoon my family drove Jackie back to her dorm and headed home. Seated on my couch, silence all around, I imagined my apartment filled with the voices of my family, a one-of-a-kind orchestra. I felt the sharp contrast between where my life was and where I wanted it to go. Deep down I knew with whom I wanted to share it with, but I also knew a life with Sarah wasn't possible.

"I'm excited for a whole night together." Sarah stood up from her round table and slid a file into her briefcase.

"Can't tonight." I slung my backpack over my shoulder. "Stuff to do." Weeks ago, I'd never have hesitated to spend the night with Sarah. Was my desire waning or had I gotten used to doing my own thing, since doing so was easier than picturing Sarah out living her other life?

"Come on, Blu. There'll always be stuff to do. Linda gets back tomorrow from Philadelphia, and this may be our last chance until who knows when."

How had my life become contingent on Linda going away for a bowling tournament or having dinner with friends? I'd accepted her role as the primary person in Sarah's life, but I was growing resentful of her status and wanted her out of the picture. Not that I was ready to announce my love for Sarah, but I'd tired of the guilt, the charade, and the fear that someone would catch us.

"Fine," I said, giving in as usual.

That evening, after shoveling Sarah's driveway, I lay on the couch, my feet on her lap, a fire roaring in the fireplace, the cats sleeping on the backs of chairs. Sarah read the newspapers and I took a GMAT quiz, which I failed, confirming my decision not to apply for an MBA. But I didn't care because:

A) I was spending my evening with someone I loved.
B) My writing was finally coming along.
C) A and B were all that mattered.

When Linda called, Sarah took the cordless into the bedroom and shut the door, leaving me with a fourth option:

D) My entire life was a lie.

"Sometimes I want to make love to you," Sarah said the next morning when I'd woken up to find her watching me. "Sometimes

I want to hold you. Sometimes I want to look at you. Sometimes I want to hear your voice, and sometimes I need to know what you're doing."

What was I doing?

That afternoon, Sarah locked our office door, then took me in her arms. "I loved having you in my bed last night. I'll miss you tonight."

"If we spend too much time together, we're going to get sick of each other." I teased.

She pulled her head back. "Are you getting sick of me?"

"A little."

"See? Perfect relationship. We don't live together." Sarah kissed me then headed home to make sure we hadn't left any incriminating evidence.

"I've always had the need to write," author Madeleine L'Engle said to the sizable audience at Smith College. "If I went somewhere, saw something, or heard about something, I needed to write it down and share my experiences." Her words resonated with me.

After the reading, Allison and I sat in her truck, waiting for it to warm up.

"It's crazy that it took Madeleine two years to get *A Wrinkle in Time* published and it was her seventh book." I thought of my expanding file of rejection letters. "Guess I need to be persistent if I want to be a writer."

"This might help." Allison handed me the *Reality Bites* soundtrack on CD. "I know how much you loved the movie."

We'd seen it together the week before and I couldn't stop quoting from it. It felt as if the movie had been written for me, as it was about recently graduated college students struggling with what to do next. My favorite line was when Ethan Hawke's character says, "All you have to be by the time you're 23 is yourself." That line would become my mantra when I felt I wasn't succeeding fast enough.

"Thanks. I love it."

"There's something I need to tell you." Allison gripped the steering wheel, stared out the windshield and let out a long breath.

"I like you as more than a friend." Even though Allison was available, in the right age bracket, and Jewish (scoring major points with Mom), there was one thing she wasn't: Sarah.

I removed my scarf, suddenly hot, and told her about Sarah, wanting her to know the reason for my rejection had nothing to do with her. Allison said she'd had a hunch after that night at Paradiso, guessing Sarah was more than my boss.

"Do you think it's wrong I'm dating an older woman?" I asked.

"Of course not. I dated a coach once. It happens."

"How much older was your coach?"

"Fifteen years."

A fraction of our age difference.

"When did you realize you were gay?" I asked.

"I'm actually bi. I also date guys."

I thought of Peter, who I'd been attracted to and would be seeing in a few weeks at Lauren's wedding. "What's that like?"

"Not like anything." Allison shrugged. "I'm drawn to a person, not body parts. I go to a women's bi group. We talk about what it's like. You should come." Was being bi the answer to my ongoing internal dilemma of my sexual identity?

"Maybe I'm bi." A calmness washed over me at the possibility.

"You could be," Allison said like it was no big deal. And I believed her.

There were two messages on my answering machine when I got home from the Madeleine L'Engle reading.

"The last fitting for the bridesmaids' dresses is this Thursday at five," Lauren said. "And since it's Saint Patrick's Day, we're going for drinks after. See you then."

The second message was from Ben.

"Great news! My editor liked your recent pieces on your grandfather. Says she'd hire you to do some freelance writing if you move to New York. So, move to New York!"

There it was, my dream, delivered via answering machine. Why wasn't I jumping for joy? Maybe because choosing my dream meant giving up my heart.

~

Friday afternoon I watched from my car as Sarah hugged Linda on the front steps of their home, then walked down her driveway, overnight bag in hand. Linda waved to me, and I waved back, guilty to the gills.

"Does Linda think the conference starts tonight?" I asked Sarah when she got into my car.

"Yes. But can we agree not to mention Linda this weekend?"

I put the car in reverse. "Linda who?"

Two-and-a-half hours later Sarah and I arrived in the Bronx. Mark was standing on Baily Avenue, holding a parking spot for my car. He wrapped me in a bear hug before giving Sarah the same greeting. I watched them, the two most special people in my life, meeting for the first time.

We dropped our bags in his apartment, then took the subway down to the West Village. Mark's boyfriend, Steven, was waiting at the restaurant. I thought anyone looking at our foursome would assume, based on our ages, Mark and I were a couple, and that Steven and Sarah were too.

After dinner, we walked to the Hudson River and gazed back at the glistening city lights. The evening felt magical. I think Sarah felt it too, because she took my head in her hands and kissed me. My first instinct was to pull away, but when none of the runners or cyclists passing by called us names, my embarrassment smoothed away and disappeared into the wide river below.

Back at Mark's, Sarah went into the bedroom, and I helped Mark make up the couch. I thanked him again for giving us his room and started to cry.

"What's wrong?" He placed his hands on my shoulders and looked down at me.

"But is this, us, real?"

"It's as real as you want it to be. Now go." He shoved me gently toward the bedroom. "Sarah's waiting."

Sarah and I left early the next morning to attend the second half of a student affairs conference in Connecticut. Our presentation was on preparing new students to meet with their faculty advisors.

Afterward I had terrible cramps, so we blew off the rest of the conference and relaxed in our hotel room.

"Do you know what gets rid of cramps?" Sarah unbuttoned my jeans. In no time, the cramps were gone.

The hot maple syrup was too good to resist, and I ate four pancakes when Sarah brought me to a sugarhouse in Shelburne Falls the following Saturday. Happy to see me eating, Sarah bought a pint of syrup, promising to make me pancakes the following Saturday.

Back at Milford, Sarah went into my apartment while I ran to the mailboxes. When I came in, she was holding a bag of red licorice.

"This was on your doormat, and it had a note taped to it," Sarah said. "I'll read it to you. 'Felice, Something sweet for someone sweet. Love, Allison.'" Sarah looked at me over her reading glasses. Normally I loved that look, but this time her gaze sent a shot to my gut. "Care to explain?"

"Nothing to explain. We're friends." I dropped my mail onto the coffee table, which had belonged to Sarah's mother.

"Does Allison like you?"

I nodded, annoyed she still insisted on digging for confirmation.

"Did you say something to give her the impression you liked her?"

"No. Why would you ask that?"

"Blu, you don't realize the way you talk to people. It makes them assume you're interested. And it's your eyes, too."

"You said my eye contact was the reason you hired me."

"It was. But your eyes can also be flirtatious."

"Sarah, it doesn't matter. I'm not interested in her." I hit my answering machine's flashing button.

"Hey, it's Allison. Did you get my present? I guess you did if you're hearing this message. Want to go to dinner? Call me."

Sarah's eyes were on fire. "Care to fill me in on what's going on?"

"I told you, we're friends. And you and I only have a few hours until you go home to your girlfriend, and I'm not giving you a hard time about that. Let's not waste the little time we have fighting."

"Are you leading her on?" Sarah folded her arms across her

chest.

"Sarah, I promise I'm not leading anybody anywhere. We talk, okay? She tells me about past girlfriends, and I tell her about this woman I'm in love with."

Sarah's expression softened. "Care to tell me about this woman?"

"I could." I took her hand. "Or I could just show you." Then I led Sarah into the bedroom, the one place we never fought.

Another snowstorm with April three days away. Unbelievable. It had been in the fifties that morning, which was why I'd driven to work, but by five the snow was coming down without pause. I decided to leave my car and take the bus home. Sarah had left early to bring soup to Linda, who had a cold. I was glad to see Sarah leave, since most of the day had been a continuation of our argument from the previous Saturday. She admitted it wasn't Allison she was concerned about per se, but anyone my age showing me how it could be different not having to hide. I resisted saying she was the one who had the power to change our situation, because that wasn't entirely true. We were both culpable. She feared hurting Linda, and I feared people's opinions.

At home I found a letter on my kitchen table.

> Hey Blu.
>
> It was a day of ups and downs. A day of questions, tears, doubts, fears. It always comes down to the fact that I can't be that "normal" relationship you need and want and are ready for no matter how much I want to be or how much I love you, and I know it makes you unhappy. I feel guilty and sad and frustrated and at a dead end. The moments we have, or steal, are so fine and in focus that most of the time I can avoid the issue until I see your unhappy eyes and hear you almost wistfully wishing for a relationship with, if not Allison, someone like her. It puts me in the place I can't escape, and I feel selfish and more morally jeopardized and even resigned and panicked. This has been going round and round, and we find ourselves with nowhere to go but into the same tears. I know this isn't what we signed on for last fall. Like I said, the highs must

> outweigh the lows and when that balance gets out of whack then—I don't want to go there. I don't want to lose you. S.

Even though I still looked forward to seeing Sarah each morning at work, and still looked forward to spending Saturdays together, the uptick in arguments made me fear that the lows were starting to tip the scale. I slid Sarah's letter into the "S" envelope in the back of my closet, cranked the heat, and called my parents.

"How's the tie business?" Dad asked.

"The alumni director ordered another dozen." In the kitchen I removed a mug with a cat on it, courtesy of Sarah's house.

"That's great, sweetheart. You know, the offer still stands to turn the basement into a tie factory. When does softball start?"

"In two weeks." I filled the tea kettle with water. "That is, if spring ever gets here."

"It will. Here's Mom. Love you."

I talked to Mom about my friend's upcoming wedding, and she shared details of the family trip she was planning to the Grand Canyon that summer, which I couldn't go on because of work. Another sign I was breaking away and becoming an adult.

The second I hung up the phone, it rang. "I've been calling you for over an hour," Sarah said.

"I was on with my mom. But how are you able to call?"

"I'm in the sunroom. Linda's sleeping. I was worried about you driving in the snow."

"I took the bus. And my apartment's freezing."

"Maybe Allison can come over and warm you."

"Why would you say that? I told you we're just friends." Sarah's accusations irritated me.

"Blu, are you going to break up with me?"

"No." I thought of my parents' recent twenty-sixth wedding anniversary. Would I ever be with someone that long? At the rate I was going, not a chance.

"Don't start cooking until you see the whites of my eyes," Sarah said when she called. The same Battle of Bunker Hill line she uttered every Saturday morning before heading to my place.

I opened all the windows. Mid-April and a warm hint of spring permeated the air, which was comforting after that endless winter. I emptied the contents of my bedroom closet onto my futon and bagged everything that was too big. Since I'd moved back to Amherst, I'd gone down one clothing size. My stomach had been against most foods coming near it.

Sarah and I watched women's college basketball on television while solving the previous week's *New York Times* Sunday crossword puzzle.

"Time for a little afternoon delight," Sarah said at halftime, leading me into the bedroom. She removed my clothes playfully, kissing each newly bared patch of skin. After all this time, my body still reacted to her touch. Sarah understood more about what turned me on than I did. I was learning about her body too. She was never hesitant to tell me what she liked, but mostly what she liked, she said, was pleasing me. I asked her if the sex was good because we were in love, or if we were in love because the sex was good, and she had laughed before saying, "Both."

As much as I enjoyed making love with Sarah, I still wasn't sure I was a lesbian. (I know, I know. If it quacks like a duck.) I wasn't attracted to other women. With Kimberly, making love had felt experimental, but with Sarah it felt right. I chalked it up to being fearful of labels, which put you in a box. Regardless of what I was, in those moments with Sarah I was happy. My favorite part was after we finished: lying with my head on Sarah's chest, the slowing tempo of her heartbeat against my cheek, not a care in the world. I'd never felt that kind of inner calm. Most of the time my brain ran sprints, my body rushing to keep up.

Art Spiegelman, on campus as part of Holocaust Remembrance Day, signed my *Maus* book. I walked away, the book clutched to my chest, and entered the Cape Cod Lounge. The room was packed with students, faculty, and administrators for the memorial service. As the program began, Kimberly rushed in and sat on my right. Sarah was seated on my left.

The first speaker, a Holocaust survivor and poet who stood about five feet, was from Poland. Her thick European accent sounded like Papa's as she read a poem about her sister, who'd died in Auschwitz. I sniffled, and Kimberly rubbed my back. I was sure Sarah would've done the same if she could.

The second speaker, Eva, a child of survivors and a local therapist, spoke of trauma being passed down from survivors to the next generations. Had trauma been passed down to me?

When the program ended, Sarah walked away to speak with the dean of students, and Kimberly gave me a hug before heading off to class. I approached Eva, who wore a loose-fitting dress. "Hi. My grandparents are—" A pocket of air lodged itself in my throat.

"It's okay." She touched my arm tenderly, a slew of silver bracelets rattled along her wrist. "Take a deep breath."

I did, then continued. "My grandparents are survivors. I'm writing about my grandfather's experience in the camps."

"Are your grandparents still alive?"

"My grandfather is. My grandmother committed—" The air bubble returned. I took another deep breath. "My grandmother took her own life. I'm named after her. My grandfather remarried another survivor. He's been telling me stories, and I've been writing them down. He cries sometimes when he talks and has nightmares from dredging up the past." I knew I was speaking fast but feared another air bubble.

"It's difficult for survivors to share what happened to them, but just know that by listening, you're helping him. I run a support group for children of survivors and would love for you to join us. A few, including myself, are concerned about passing this trauma on to our children, the grandchildren. It could be helpful for them to hear from you." She smiled since my eyes had welled up with tears. "And I'm guessing it may be good for you too."

Eva lived in a contemporary home deep in the woods of North Amherst. Her sunken living room had a wall of windows that faced a forest of lean trees, tiny green buds visible on the ends of branches. Bronze sculptures of torsos, ranging in size from a few inches to a few feet, were scattered around the interior. Her husband was the artist.

The group consisted of three women, one man, and Eva. I was the youngest by at least twenty years. After brief introductions, Eva asked me if I thought I had been affected emotionally by what my grandparents had endured in the camps. "Their trauma," I said, "had no doubt influenced the way they'd raised my mother, who in turn raised me, but my mother tried to shield me and my sisters from the amount of fear and worry that had been passed on to her. But she couldn't shield us forever. In college, I learned the truth about how my grandmother had died."

When Mom was eighteen, her mother, after years of depression caused by her time in the Lodz Ghetto and Auschwitz Concentration Camp, had committed suicide by hanging herself. Mom and Uncle Mark, who was six at the time, had found her. Since taking one's life is a violation of Jewish law, Papa, fearful of the stigma, had made his children say their mother had died of cancer. He had made them keep a secret about the most horrible thing in their lives. As I revealed this, it hit me: no wonder I couldn't come clean about Sarah; keeping secrets ran in my family.

When the session ended, Eva said she was glad I'd come.

Without planning to I blurted, "I'm having an affair with a much older woman who lives with her girlfriend, and I'm not sure what to do. Can I see you as a therapist?"

"That's not my area," Eva said, "but I have a colleague who could help."

"How did the Holocaust group go?" Sarah asked the next morning at work.

"I told Eva about us. She suggested I see a therapist."

"Be warned," Sarah said. "They always blame the mother."

"Have you been to therapy before?" asked Barbara. My new therapist's long bushy black hair had a white skunk stripe starting at her right temple.

"Once. In college." I sat in an indentation on a soft, tan couch. The walls were taupe. A tall plant near the window was a pale green. Barbara's matching tunic and pants were beige. Everything about the room was neutral. Was that intentional?

"And what issue brought you there?" She cracked open a thick notebook and clicked open her pen.

"The question of how to tell whether you're gay."

"Is that why you're here today? Are you still questioning whether you're gay?" Her stare was direct, but gentle.

I shook my head. "I've decided I'm bi." After that conversation with Allison, I'd gone with her to a bi group meeting. There were a dozen women, ranging in ages from twenty to fifty. One was a married mother of two who had fallen in love with a woman. Another said she was physically attracted to men and emotionally attracted to women. But most, like me, were attracted to both. It had been helpful to hear their stories, and gave me an awareness that life was an endless road of choices that could be changed, and changed again.

"Then what brings you here today?" Barbara asked.

Balling one hand inside the other, I rested them in my lap. "I'm secretly seeing a woman with a girlfriend, and she's—" I caught the dates on the framed college degrees on the wall. Barbara was Sarah's age, give or take a year. She might know Sarah. Or Linda. I wished I'd gone to a male therapist. Why hadn't I thought of that? But wait, I didn't have to give Sarah's name. "She's older."

"How much older?"

Was Barbara fishing for confirmation? Had Linda bugged the office?

"Does it matter?" I asked.

"No. But it could shed insight."

Insight into what? How messed up I was?

"She's thirty-four years older," I said, expecting Barbara to topple out of her seat and onto the floor. And though her eyes flashed wider for a second, she recovered quickly.

"And how old are you?"

"Twenty-three. Is that bad? It's bad, right?"

"No." She shook her head. "The difference in age isn't bad. But the affair, well, that's not good."

"I know." I slumped back and stared out the window at the cars driving through Northampton.

"I'll be honest with you: it's a sizeable age gap. But that doesn't make it wrong. Tell me." Barbara clicked her pen. "How's your relationship with your mother?"

I'd have to tell Sarah she had been right.

After our final golf lesson, Sarah and I sat in the near-empty parking lot of Holyoke Community College watching the sky melt into a red and orange puddle behind the blurred mountain ridge in the distance. We were eating peanut-butter crackers, a poor substitute for dinner.

"Did you know the Mount Holyoke Range is the only part of the Metacomet Ridge that runs east to west?" Sarah gestured ahead.

"Uh-huh." I checked my watch.

"Have somewhere to be, Blu?"

"You know I don't like the car thing." Eight months in, and we were still meeting in our cars. I still enjoyed our time together, but the time together I wanted was to be spent doing things, not hiding out in parked cars.

"I don't think of it as a car thing." Sarah took my hand. "But as time spent with you."

"Which is more of a problem for you?" Barbara asked at our second appointment. "The age difference or that she's in another relationship?"

"In another relationship. And her name's Sarah." Mark had convinced me that if I was making the effort to attend therapy, I might as well be honest.

"So, you're okay with the age difference?"

"It's not ideal, but my issue is more what other people will think." I picked at the cuticle on my left thumbnail.

"And what will they think?" Barbara asked. A tingling appeared in my nostrils, the first indication that tears were forthcoming. "Felice, what will people think if they find out you're dating an older woman?" Her voice gentle, but forceful. I needed pushing. She knew that. A tear dripped onto my cheek. "It's okay. You can tell me."

I stared at my inflamed thumb. "That there's something wrong with me." I truly thought there was. I'd never seen two women together with such a large age difference. As far as I knew, we were the only ones.

"Why would dating an older woman make people think there was something wrong with you?"

"Because it's not right."

"Says who?" Barbara asked.

"I'm not saying it's against the law, but people would question why I'd want to be with someone so much older. Especially my parents. That's why I can't tell anyone. Well, that and because Sarah has a girlfriend."

"Okay," Barbara said. "I know you're an athlete, so I want you to imagine that you just won a gold medal in the Olympics. How would you feel?"

Finally, an easy question. "I'd be psyched."

Barbara smiled and nodded. "Good. That's the correct response for such a tremendous accomplishment. But this gold medal comes with a catch. You can't tell anyone you won it." She paused. "Now, would you still feel the same about winning it?"

I swallowed down a lump in my throat, her analogy hitting me like a punch to the solar plexus.

"Felice," she continued. "Love doesn't come easily, which is why when you fall in love you're filled with this immense happiness and your first instinct is to share it with everyone. That's one of the reasons people have weddings. To experience what it feels like to have their love recognized and validated. In your situation, you're having all the normal feelings, but you're forced to hide them. Keeping love a secret is the opposite of what love is about. And until you can love openly, you'll never truly be happy."

I heard her words, but I wouldn't understand what she was saying until long after I'd repeated this behavior more times than I'd like to admit.

Our first two softball practices had been canceled because of inclement weather, which put us behind schedule. So, by the third date, despite the forecast calling for rain, Rachel said practice was a go.

Halfway through, it poured. We scrambled to our cars. I sat in mine with heat blasting and removed my muddy cleats when someone tapped on my window. I rolled it down.

"Hi, I'm Joanne." Joanne had played second base. We hadn't talked, but during one play she had yelled forcefully to me in centerfield, "Put it right here!" which had made me nervous that I might not be able to do something I'd been doing skillfully for years. "It's Felice, right?"

I nodded, surprised she'd remembered my name.

Joanne bent down so our eyes were level as water dripped off the lip of her golf umbrella. She had a tiny birthmark above her lip. "You're really good. Strong arm."

"Thanks." I felt heat rise to my cheeks. "You are too."

"Would you be up for getting coffee this weekend? There's this cute shop near my house."

Was she asking me out?

"Sorry. I have a wedding."

"Hope it's not yours." She grinned.

"No. College friend."

"Another time then?"

"Sure."

"Great," Joanne said. "I'll call you."

"I'm so proud of each of you," said Olivia at our last writing class. "You've shown major improvement, and I encourage you all to submit something soon."

Before I left, Olivia gave me a slip of paper with a phone number on it that belonged to a friend of hers, an editor at a Jewish literary journal. "I told her you were writing about your grandfather's experiences in the Holocaust. She's interested in talking with you. Call her. I believe you've got something special."

"Another classic for you to read." Sarah handed me the paperback *Patience and Sarah.* We were sitting in my car behind the Village Commons, watching people eating egg sandwiches outside the Tailgate Picnic deli.

"Are you trying to tell me I need patience to be with you?"

"No," Sarah said. "It's me who needs patience. At least today. I look forward to spending every Saturday with you, so it's hard to miss even one."

"You've known about this wedding for months."

"I know." Sarah placed her hand on my thigh. "I'm just disappointed since I won't see you for a week."

"Did you forget that's because you're leaving tomorrow to go on vacation with Linda?"

Sarah's hand slid into the crevice of my crotch. "I wish it was you coming with me."

"Then why isn't it?" I stopped her hand as I felt myself getting turned on. It didn't take much when it came to Sarah.

"Promise me you won't get any crazy ideas at this wedding."

"Such as?"

Sarah nodded to my bridesmaid outfit hanging in the backseat. "Getting married."

At the rear of the massive Catholic church, the wedding planner lined us up in twos, then sent me and Peter arm in arm down the lengthy aisle. I'd been anxious about seeing Peter since I'd given him the brush-off in November, but he seemed happy to see me.

After the ceremony, I accompanied Lauren to the bathroom.

"Peter asked me if you were still dating that guy." Lauren reapplied her lipstick while looking at me in the mirror. "What guy? You never told me about a guy."

"I lied. I wasn't up for a long-distance relationship." I stared back at her, not daring to look at myself in the hideous green bridesmaid dress.

"Well, Peter still likes you." She blotted her lips. "You should give him a chance. It's better than being alone."

But I wasn't alone.

We walked outside to the limo, where the wedding party was waiting. I sat between my former editor, Ben, and my one-time date, Peter.

"Why do married women always cry at weddings?" Ben asked.

"Because they're aware of what the brides are in for," I replied.

He laughed. "You've got to use that in a future column. Speaking of which, my editor said to call her when you're settled in New York."

"You're moving to New York?" asked Peter.

"Not sure yet. I'm committed to UMass through the summer."

"September's a great time for starting something new," Ben said.

Lauren tapped on her champagne flute, using her shiny wedding band. "Charlie and I thank you all for being in our wedding, and we look forward to celebrating at yours."

Glasses clinked, and tears clouded my vision as I looked around at my friends. Would they honestly look forward to celebrating at my wedding if it were to Sarah? Would they buy dresses, rent tuxes, reserve hotel rooms, travel across the country, and spend their hard-earned savings on gifts? I thought of what Barbara had said, that people have weddings to share their love and to get that love back. But what if we had a wedding and that love wasn't mirrored? What if people just looked uncomfortable?

April 26, 1994

Blu,

Why does every day start with images of how and when I'll see you and have a chance to touch and kiss you? And why does every day end with a rewind of the times and feelings of our time together—wishing it were more—wishing for time to stop? Or for any natural disaster that could keep us cuddled on the futon wrapped in each other's arms and bodies in candlelight or no light or just the light in your eyes—soft and tender after love. Where does this longing come from that yearns to hear your voice or see your curly head across the room or on my chest? To see those great legs on the golf course or around my hips? Why do I seemingly need to feel your softness and wetness and smoothness against my skin? And why does kissing you, either gently or with mounting passion, become an end in itself with a life of its own? And whether or not it leads to making love, it leaves me feeling warm and fulfilled and happy. Why? S.

"I feel guilty all the time," I said to Barbara, sitting in what I now referred to as the "hot seat."

"Because of the affair?" She opened her notebook.

"Yes. But also because my mom said to 'find a nice Jewish girl.' I know she was joking, but it's another reason for them to be disappointed."

"Is it important for you to marry someone Jewish?"

"I always thought I would, but now marriage doesn't even seem like something I want." I continued to dig at the now mutilated cuticle on my thumb.

"And what is it you want?"

I slid my hands under my thighs to prevent further damage. "To be a writer. But even doing that makes me feel guilty because it's time I should spend working."

"Aren't you writing about your grandfather being in the Holocaust?"

"Yes, but it's not a real job like the one at UMass."

"What do you mean by real?"

"Official. I signed a contract."

"Does something need to be official to be real?" Barbara clicked her pen, a habit she had after asking me tough questions.

"Doesn't it?"

"You often refer to your relationship with Sarah as not real. While the relationship may not be official—" Barbara gestured air quotes "—the love you have for Sarah is real. If you could officially marry Sarah, would you want to?"

I pictured the displeasure on my parents' faces. The awkward stares from my friends. "No."

"Are you saying no because you wouldn't want to? Or because it's easier to reject something you do want to avoid feeling disappointed when you think you can't have it?" Barbara had my number. She knew how my head worked. I looked at my watch. Twenty minutes left. "Felice," Barbara continued. "I know talking about this makes you uncomfortable and that you'd rather be doing a million other things than sharing your feelings, but this is important." A fat pigeon landed on the windowsill and began pecking against the glass. We both looked over, and I was thankful for the momentary break in questioning. "When you think about how people might react to you and Sarah, how do you reconcile that feeling? What do you do?"

I shrugged. "I organize stuff. Read. Do puzzles."

"You keep busy to avoid facing your thoughts." It wasn't a question.

"I've always been productive."

"And there's nothing wrong with that," Barbara said. "But do you ever counteract your busyness with downtime?"

"I ride my bike and go to the gym."

"That's still doing something. Do you ever do nothing?"

"I sleep."

Barbara shook her head. "No. I mean just be?"

"Just be what?"

"Just be still."

"That's a thing?"

She smiled. "I'd like you to practice being still for two minutes a day. You can do this anywhere. Close your eyes and breathe through your nose. Think of the word 'in" as you inhale and the word 'out" as you exhale. Taking a thoughtful break can help us step away from what's hurting or distracting us and allow us to see things clearly. It may also help you understand what you're trying to avoid by not expressing yourself."

I understood perfectly well what I was trying to avoid: the idea of a life without Sarah.

> May 3, 1994
>
> Hey Blu,
>
> Missing your smile and wanting to say to you, "Look, the sun is going, going, boom, gone" and watch it go with you in my arms, your hair in my face, and seeing the brilliant red reflections of the ocean on your cheek and feeling my heart soar like the osprey that flies out chasing the sunset. How can we make the time slow down when we're together? Keep dreaming of the next few days we have when I get back and I can look into your eyes and hold your hand and kiss your daytime and nighttime lips and hold your body to mine and for a few days, our time will be our time. Almost there. S.

"Machines are not our friends," Kurt Vonnegut Jr. said to the sold-out crowd at the UMass Fine Arts Center. Allison and I were seated in the fourth row, staring up at his unbrushed gray hair and his matching thick mustache. "We need extended families again, cousins and relatives. We should all have puberty ceremonies; they would do a lot for our community. Only practicing Jews and some Indian tribes do this. We must tell our kids, 'You're a man and woman now. Act like one.'"

The audience—mostly college students—clapped.

"I know you're all wondering how you get grants and advances. You don't, so forget them. You want to know where you get money? You inherit it." Kurt's cynicism was on fire, but he had yet to say anything about writing, which was how his talk had been billed. Then he added, "Becoming a writer may be a lost cause because of television."

"But don't writers write TV shows?" someone shouted. Kurt either ignored the comment or didn't hear it as he gazed around the massive auditorium.

"I understand kids today. Your burning question is, 'Does penis size really matter?'" Laughter filled the venue. "We ultimately are here on earth to fart around, and don't let anyone tell you different."

I was left with a feeling of cold water on my face, as though he had been speaking directly to me, saying, "You and your so-called writing talent are on your own, motherfucker!" No one was going to be telling me what to do or how to do it. If I wanted to accomplish anything, I had to figure it out myself.

Saturday night I picked Sarah up from Bradley Airport. Linda was staying on a few extra nights in Florida, as usual, with friends. I was excited to get to play house with Sarah for two nights.

"Hello, boys, mama's home." Sarah greeted each cat with a kiss before carrying her luggage into the bedroom, me close behind.

"Tell me about your trip." I got into my side (fine, Linda's side) of the bed.

"It was okay." Sarah unzipped her suitcase and removed her blue-and-white toiletry bag. "I spent the entire time counting down the minutes until I could see you."

While Sarah showered, I practiced my breathing, per Barbara's instructions. After two minutes, to my surprise, a stillness settled through me.

Sarah came into the bedroom, tossed her robe onto the bed, and pulled back the covers. Just as our bodies were fitting together, the phone rang. She grabbed her bathrobe and the phone, and walked out to talk to Linda. My calmness flew out the window. Why did I continue to torture myself?

"Now, where were we?" Sarah got back into bed minutes later as though the call had never happened. Then she saw my face. "What's wrong, Blu?"

"I feel cheated. You have everything. A home, vacations, anniversaries, and what do I have? Letters hidden in my closet. The truth concealed in my heart. All I do is wait for any chance I can get to be with you. What kind of life is that?" I slapped my hands on the bed. Cody and Sammy, curled near my feet, lifted their heads. "I hate that the little time we have is rushed. That I'm constantly wondering when we'll meet again and never appreciating the time we have. I'm also having second thoughts about working again as the night director this summer. It's hard being around you. I want you before work *and* after work. Sneaking around makes me feel as though I don't exist. If you loved me, then—" I stopped as I always did, but my anger gave me a surge of confidence. "You'd let me go." As the words left my mouth, it became clear, like the clean daylight when clouds have passed, that my freedom was altogether my decision. I didn't need to be "let go." I only needed to let go.

"Perhaps you're right." Sarah shrank back onto her stack of pillows as though the air inside her had escaped. "I only seem to make it harder for you. I've been such a fool. Go back to your life."

What life?

I reached for her, my heart filling with dread at the thought of a future in which we were no longer together. Our hands were soon touching, grabbing, tugging each other closer, our tears and fears fueling our passion, sadness our new foreplay. No gentle kisses or caresses, just harried movements fueled by anger and needs. We were trying to merge into one, as though that would prove we belonged together, as though that would make it right.

We split apart, our breathing rapid, energy depleted, like animals after a fight. Sex had become our go-to cure to assuage arguments. If we were any other couple, we would've met each other's friends by now, maybe moved in together, started planning a future. But that wasn't possible. Not for us.

"Blu." Sarah sighed into the darkness. "My life has changed because of you, and if it were doable, I'd change even more for you. The problem is I have thirty years too many wrinkles. Hearing you say you want out makes it sound like I put you in a place you don't want to be. And since I'm in love with you, I should try to help by doing something. But what?"

By deciding: Linda or me.

But Sarah would never leave Linda. I recognized that now. I might've been her heart, but Linda was her family, and that pull was stronger. Sarah had committed herself to Linda years ago. They might've had a sexless union, but they had a life together, a home, cats, friends. I couldn't compete with that. If I were to have any peace, I had to end it. It would be hard, but it would only get harder. I'd break up with Sarah in the morning. What other choice did I have besides more heartache? With my decision made, I fell into a deep sleep, certain this would be our last night together.

Between a Rock and a Really Hard Place
May 1994–August 1994

The shouting woke me. I bolted upright and reached for Sarah but found only cool, rumpled sheets. I squinted at the cable box. It glowed a blurry 2:48 a.m. I was about to call out for Sarah when the shouting stopped. Silence, except for the low purring of the cats on the bed. I relaxed, assuming it was the television. But soon the shouting picked up again, and I heard Sarah trying to quiet the source. Who was screaming?

Then I knew. Linda, the legitimate partner, the one expected to be away two more days, had come home in the middle of the night. She'd seen us in their bed. We'd been caught. The truth exposed. The cat was out of the bag.

I dressed in the dark, my trembling hands fumbling to button my jeans. A shadow appeared through the fabric covering on the French doors. I held my breath. My personal Hitchcock movie. Only after Sarah slipped inside did I exhale.

"Linda's home," Sarah said with perfect composure, sliding her hands into the pockets of her bathrobe, the same robe she'd removed hours earlier in her hurry to make love to me.

"I'm sorry."

"You have nothing to be sorry about. You did nothing wrong." Sarah brushed her hand across my cheek. "I'll call you."

As I was leaving, I was hesitant to look in the sunroom but saw

Linda anyway, crestfallen on the chaise, head in her hands. That was our doing. I'd thought I was a kind person. Not even close.

Outside I half expected my tires to be slashed. But Linda was too nice to do something that spiteful.

On the drive home, except for a few glassy-eyed raccoons and possums crossing the road, the streets were empty. Who else but rodents and cheaters would be out in the middle of the night? At the top of the Notch, I pulled over, opened my car door, and threw up on the side of the road. Nauseated as I was, I was also relieved. Now the lies could stop. At least that's what I thought.

"I confessed everything, Blu." Sarah called later that morning from the pay phone at the deli when she picked up the *Times*. The same phone she'd called me from every Sunday for the last few months.

I pulled the covers over my head as though that would shield me from the mess my life had become. "What's going to happen now?"

"Not sure." I pictured Sarah running her free hand through her hair. "But whatever happens, it doesn't change how I feel about you. I still love you." Sarah promised to call later and hung up. My stomach churned. Had Linda not caught us, would I have really broken up with Sarah that morning? Who was I kidding.

I called the only person I could in that situation. "Linda found us in bed together last night. I feel sick."

"But isn't that a good thing?" Mark said. "Now you can be together."

"How? Once everyone finds out I'm the reason they broke up they're all going to hate me." I curled into a fetal position to alleviate the pain sluicing through my abdomen. "Am I messed up or what?"

"Not at all. This isn't easy. But this angst you're feeling would go away if you said, 'screw it' to what others thought."

As if I could just snap my fingers and years of worrying what others thought about me would simply vanish. Changing behavior doesn't happen overnight. Even now, decades later, I still care about the judgement of others. Isn't it human nature to want to be liked?

~

The next morning, I drove to work with the windows open. The warmth of May in the Happy Valley filled my heart with expectation. Fruit and vegetable stands reappeared at the ends of driveways; downtown stores rolled wares onto sidewalks; and college seniors prepared to face the real world. Everything moved in a cycle, including my life. I'd set up the same routine as last summer: orientation sessions and trysts, only now with Sarah, not Kimberly. Did I want to go through that again?

"Say-rah called in sick." Peg walked into our office holding a sheet of paper. "She sounded tay-rible. I told her to stay in bed." Same advice Peg gave Sarah last fall. Only difference? That time I'd been in Sarah's bed with her. Peg handed me a list of what Sarah needed me to do in preparation for orientation training week, but I had my own list: What was happening at Sarah's house? Were they working things out? Was Linda leaving? And if she was, what did that mean for me?

"It was awful," I said to Barbara, rocking nervously on the couch. "I can still hear Linda yelling, 'How could you? Why would you do this to us?' It plays on a loop in my head. She didn't deserve this. We're monsters."

"You're not monsters. But you must've considered what would happen if Linda found out."

"I kind of hoped she'd meet someone else and break up with Sarah first." My heart pounded. "I can't breathe."

Barbara closed her notebook and tucked it into the cushion beside her hip, then set both hands on her knees. "Have you been working on your breathing exercises?"

I nodded.

"Good. Let's try it together." Barbara audibly inhaled and exhaled. I closed my eyes and followed along. After a minute or two she said, "Now I'd like you to picture a place from your childhood that made you happy. When you've got it, describe it to me."

The image of the baseball field at my elementary school, where I'd played Little League, appeared. The all-dirt infield and the forest-green dugout with my teammates cheering from inside, their tiny fingers knitted between the chicken-wire covering. I'd built my confidence on that field. It's where I'd fallen in love with playing ball.

"How are you feeling now?" Barbara asked.

"Calmer."

"Great. The next time you're upset, picture that field while practicing your breathing. Use it as a reminder that you're capable of being happy. It won't make the issues go away, but it will calm you down enough to deal with them."

"Want to go to Provincetown with me this weekend?" Joanne asked after our softball game. I was sitting on the bench, digging out clumps of grass from my cleats. Two weeks before she'd suggested we get coffee but had never followed up. She was certainly skipping a few steps.

"Thanks, but I have tentative plans." Sarah had said the situation at her house had settled down, but I was clueless as to what that meant for our relationship. And since we'd shared almost every Saturday together, I assumed if things had calmed down we'd continue to do so.

"Any chance you can change them?" Joanne pressed.

Change them? It had never occurred to me to change my plans on Sarah. I tossed a cleat into my bag. "Maybe."

"Why would I blow off a Saturday with Sarah to go away with a stranger?" I asked Mark, who I called the second I got home.

"Perhaps because the shit has hit the fan, and this offers a way of avoiding that?"

Yeah, that sounded about right.

"What does Joanne do?" he asked.

"An associate director in Student Services."

"Any update on the Linda situation?"

I sat on the edge of the tub and turned on the faucet. "Sarah says they're trying to work things out but that sporadically Linda will fly into a rage and threaten to leave."

"Do you want Linda to move out?" Mark said.

"No."

"Do you mean that?"

I switched on the shower. "No."

~

"Friends invited me to go to P-town this weekend. I thought it might give you and Linda time to talk." It seemed strange lying to Sarah, of all people. Was I now incapable of not lying? We were in bed, and back to our routine: Milford for "lunch" and behaving as though nothing had happened. But, of course, something huge had happened.

"Linda's done talking." Sarah was on her back, staring up at the ceiling. "She says she needs time to reflect and, ironically, she's also going away this weekend."

"I'm sorry." I lifted my head from atop her chest and looked into Sarah's eyes, tinged pink from crying. "If it weren't for me, this wouldn't be happening. I don't have to go to P-town."

"Listen to me." The sadness in Sarah's voice switching to sternness. "None of this is your fault. Yes, I hate to not spend one Saturday with you, but I want you to have fun with your friends. Though I admit I'm afraid of you meeting someone."

Joanne's two-bedroom condo in Provincetown overlooked Cape Cod Bay. The walls and furniture were bright white, and on every shelf was a nautical doodad, like a whale-shaped paper weight or a mini lighthouse. She'd said to pack bed linens, letting me know I had a room to myself. From that, I'd assumed she'd invited me as a friend.

While Joanne made her bed, I stood on the deck, not wanting to waste one minute of Cape Cod daylight. Inhaling the salty air, I gazed at the blue water and even bluer sky and practiced my breathing. It was becoming easier to rest my mind.

That evening we walked along Commercial Street. Memorial Day weekend had more people than when Sarah and I had visited the previous winter, but still nowhere near as busy as July and August.

We listened to live music inside The Crown & Anchor Inn, a hotel and entertainment complex that in the nineteenth century had a reputation for thievery and assault. Seated at a small table, we listened to Nancy Day, a local musician, sing original songs and play the piano.

"Come on, live a little," Joanne said, after I ordered a ginger ale. I changed my order to a Cape Codder, figuring the drink fit the location. Joanne ordered a Southern Comfort. "My drink," she said, as though bragging.

"Another?" The cocktail waitress picked up my empty glass minutes later. One reason I didn't drink was because, as with everything else I did, I did it fast.

"No thanks."

"Bring her one." Joanne instructed the waitress, then winked at me, saying, "I promise not to take advantage of you."

Was she serious?

Over dinner, Joanne ordered another Southern Comfort. I stuck with water. Back at her condo we sat on the couch and watched the 11 o'clock news.

"Hey," she said when I'd drifted off. "You should go to sleep."

"I should've made my bed earlier."

"That's okay. You can sleep in mine." Joanne reached out her hands and lifted me up. We stood facing each other, inches apart. Her green eyes were glassy, and her breath reeked of alcohol. "I'm glad you came with me this weekend."

Not knowing what to say, I smiled. Taking that as consent, Joanne led me down the hallway, past my room. The second we got into her bed, she became an octopus, hands coming at me from every direction.

"I need to go slow," I said, then told her about Sarah, saying we were pretty much over, but not totally.

"I understand. I'm not going anywhere." Joanne soon fell asleep, snoring into my ear.

The morning sun shone down through a narrow skylight. It took me a moment to remember where I was: sepia-colored prints of rope knots, a tiny sailboat on the dresser, and Joanne, head in hand, studying me as Sarah used to do.

"Can I tell you something?" Joanne's hair had matted to her forehead. "I've liked you since last summer when I watched you directing counselors in the quad."

"No way."

"Yes, way." She climbed on top of me, ignoring my request from the night before. She was solid, heavier than I'd expected. I'd grown used to Sarah's slight frame, almost weightless in comparison. She began to dry hump my thigh, breathing heavily. I stared up at the clouds gently rolling past and thought of Sarah concerned about me meeting someone else.

We spent the sunny day going into shops, eating free fudge samples, and people watching. Inside Womencrafts I selected a few books and asked Joanne if she'd read them.

"Not much of a reader," she said. I eyed my ring, missing Sarah's articulate and educated banter.

Back at the condo, after a lunch of fried clams, Joanne napped, and I wrote in my journal, imagining myself as her girlfriend. She was ten years older, enough to have a sense of herself, but not enough to raise eyebrows. Joanne was obviously into me, but my thoughts, still homed in on Sarah, held me back.

We returned to the Crown and Anchor that evening. As the same singer energetically belted out tunes, Joanne placed a jewelry box on the table.

Jewelry after one night of kissing?

I opened the lid, and a gold-link bracelet caught the light. Did accepting it mean I was agreeing to be her girlfriend? Joanne removed the bracelet and held it out, waiting for me to offer my wrist. Once she closed the clasp, she patted the back of my hand as though we'd sealed some pact.

Later that night, back in bed, Joanne was once again all over me, but neither my head nor heart was into it. Had I come to Provincetown hoping to be distracted by Joanne as a means of coping with a possible break up with Sarah? What better way than with a fresh beginning? It's what I'd done when I'd broken up with my high school boyfriend and walked straight into Josh's arms. And when I'd leapt from Kimberly to Sarah. That time, though, I'd been eager to switch partners. Sarah had been my private university, and I'd been more than happy to learn. Lying in bed with Joanne felt as if I'd somehow flunked out.

"What are you doing with the rest of your life?" Joanne was staring down at me again the next morning. Before I could respond, she slipped her hand up my shirt.

"Slow, remember?"

"Sorry." She removed her hand. "But don't forget, I'm not going anywhere." That time the tone in her voice made the words come across as a threat.

During the third inning of our softball game late that afternoon in Amherst, Sarah showed up and sat in the bleachers.

"Are you glad to see me?" Sarah said when I sprinted over to her after the game.

"You really need to ask?"

"No, sorry. Want to grab dinner?"

"Sure," I said, even though I had plans with Joanne. "I'll meet you at your car." I ran over to Joanne.

"Can't go to dinner, huh?" Joanne was sitting on the bench, legs extended, arms crossed.

"I'm sorry. Sarah needs to talk."

"I feel funny," Joanne said. Join the club, I wanted to say.

"Do you like that woman from your softball team?" Sarah asked. We were in bed, me spooning her from behind. We'd gone to Milford right from the game, skipping dinner.

"Why would you ask me that?"

"I get this sense you're slipping away, and that any day you'll wake up and realize you'd rather be with someone your own age. I can't blame you after all that's happened with Linda."

"What's the latest with Linda?" I was happy to redirect the conversation.

"She wants to work things out. Says this is her home and she doesn't want to leave." Hearing we hadn't destroyed Linda's entire life soothed my conscience. Yet now a new branch of guilt had materialized, thanks to the Joanne lie.

I wrapped my fingers around one of Sarah's breasts, letting it meld to my palm. "Have I ever told you you've ruined sex with anyone else?" I regretted the words immediately, realizing I might've revealed too much.

~

"I have good news." Sarah placed her "No Whining" sign into one of several cardboard boxes spread around our office. It was early June, and we were packing for our move to Crabtree Hall for the summer. "Approval came through to hire you as a permanent employee."

"Do I have to decide right now?" I slid a stack of housing brochures into a box.

"Blu, what's the hesitation?"

What's the hesitation? How could we continue doing what we were doing when I had no clue what we were doing?

Sarah looked over my shoulder. "Can I help you?"

"Just here to get Felice." Joanne was standing in the doorway, hands casually tucked inside the pockets of her khakis.

I shot to my feet. "Lunch. Softball team. I'll finish packing later."

Outside, Joanne said, "I take it you haven't told Sarah about us."

What us? Okay, I might've given Joanne the wrong impression by sleeping in her bed, but we hadn't had sex. Plus, I'd told her I was still dealing with Sarah. As much as I admired Joanne's assertiveness, there was a fine line between assertive and pushy.

"There's not an 'us' yet," I said.

"Well, I'm not going anywhere." How could I forget when she kept reminding me?

We picked up sandwiches from the Newman Center and ate by the Campus Pond. Canadian geese wandered the shoreline as students walked the crisscross paths to summer classes.

"I know you want to be a writer, so I got this for you." Joanne handed me *Starting from Scratch: A Different Kind of Writers' Manual* by Rita Mae Brown.

"Thanks. I love her books." I opened the cover to read Joanne's inscription, but she'd written nothing.

When I returned to the office, Sarah had left for the day, but she'd left a note on my desk.

> Blu-
>
> "She came at that precise junction in a life/when the past is unbearable/and the future uncertain." Time for a re-visit to Rita Mae. She speaks to us. S.

Was this a joke? Rita Mae Brown twice in less than an hour? Was the universe trying to tell me something?

We were halfway through training week and as a treat for the staff, I'd had subs delivered from a restaurant in Amherst. I handed them out in the lobby of Crabtree.

"My tuna sub isn't toasted," Sarah said, as if it were my fault. Without responding, I walked into our office. Before I shut the door, I heard Peg ask Sarah if I was okay.

"Premenstrual," Sarah said.

"Ah, yes," Peg quipped. "The good old days."

I called Mark. "I can't stand Sarah. She makes me so angry."

"What happened?"

"She blamed me for her sub not being toasted." I picked up a note Sarah had left on my desk: two smiley faces with a heart in between. I crumpled it up and tossed it into the trash.

"For that you hate her?"

"It was her tone. Implying I'm an idiot. We've been fighting over the stupidest stuff lately, then make up and have sex. It's exhausting. On Saturday we fought over if we should go out for lunch, but still had sex. Argued on Sunday about keys, then had sex right before the session started. And on Tuesday, we had some ridiculous dispute about what I can't even remember, but still slept together. What's wrong with this picture?"

"Heck," my uncle said. "What's right with it?"

That night during our softball game I dove for a shallow fly ball and my lower back locked up. Helping me limp off the field, Joanne suggested I come over for a massage. I should've turned down her offer, knowing "massage" was lesbian lingo for foreplay, but I was desperate. My back was in knots.

Joanne kneaded my muscles as I lay face down on her bed. I moaned, then bit my lip. Around her I needed to be careful of any misrepresentation of feelings. I still wasn't sure I liked her like that.

"Why don't you sleep over?" Joanne offered.

"Thanks, but I should go home." I moved to get up, but a spasm kept me prone.

"Don't think you have a choice." Joanne gave me a muscle

relaxer. In minutes the pain in my back loosened. As I drifted off to sleep, I wished for a cure to ease the pain in my heart, but no pill could do that.

Early the next morning, my back better, I drove home to get ready before work. On my kitchen table I found a note.

> Blu,
> I've been noticing you pulling away ever since you got back from P-town, like you want to get out sooner rather than later, so I'll make it easier for you. We should cool it. Good luck in your life. S.

Nausea crept up into my throat. Sarah must've stopped by on her way to work and assumed where I was. She wasn't stupid. She'd been playing this game longer than I'd been alive.

I took a quick shower, dressed in a flash, and flew to work. Sarah was seated at her desk. The second I stepped into the office, I explained that I had been out for a bike ride that morning when she'd stopped by. Sarah didn't bother looking at me, just raised her hand to stop me from speaking. She knew I was lying.

"Aren't we going to talk?" I said.

"What's there to talk about, Blu? You're in love with someone else."

"The only person I'm in love with is you, but I hate when you talk down to me like you did yesterday."

Sarah removed her glasses, and turned to face me. "I'm sorry. It's not my intent. It may be that when we're around others I feel it must have some element of employer-slash-employee, or they're going to notice what's really there. I'll work on it."

"Work harder." I grinned to show I forgave her.

"Okay. From now on, if I do or say anything that makes you feel that way, you have my permission to call me on it. Deal?"

"Deal." I walked over to the door, and, for the first time, I shut and locked it. Then I took Sarah in my arms and kissed her. She kissed me back. The breakup was off. All was normal again. And by normal, I meant we would continue the lies, continue our affair, and continue hurting Linda. This was less painful than having

Sarah look at me without love in her eyes, a look I'd become reliant on, was disoriented without. It was her pining for me that kept me coming back. Sarah—this confident, authoritative figure whom others revered—was putty in my hands. Love, I'd learned, was powerful. And when someone powerful loves you, it's as though they've handed you the key to the world.

"I went to Provincetown last weekend with a woman named Joanne," I told Barbara. "She wants me to be her girlfriend."

Barbara nodded deliberately. "This seems to be your pattern when you want to get out of a relationship, isn't it? You jump into a new one."

"At least I'm consistent."

Barbara didn't laugh. "Does Joanne know about Sarah?"

"Yes. I told her things were ending and that I needed to take it slow."

"And did you tell Sarah about Joanne?"

"God, no."

"Why not?" Barbara crossed her legs. Her long toes peeked over the top of her sandals. "Could it be you don't really want to end things with Sarah?"

I shrugged.

"Tell me about Joanne. What is it about her you're attracted to?"

"She fills that part that's missing with Sarah. Like being able to make plans to do stuff or to talk on the phone when I want."

"Do you want to be with someone who's a substitute for someone you love? Or be with someone you love?"

"But that's just it. I can't be with Sarah."

"Why not?" A warm breeze wafted in through the open window. I closed my eyes, enjoying the momentary calmness. Click went Barbara's pen.

I opened my eyes. "Because it's not right."

Barbara frowned. "Says who?"

"Um, says everyone?" My inflection hinted at obnoxious teenager. "I've never seen movies or books where the characters look like we do. And Sarah doesn't know any couples like us, and she knows every lesbian. It doesn't exist."

Barbara rubbed her chin. "Do you know why Eva suggested me

as a therapist?"

"Because you're trained at working with gay issues?"

"Yes, but there's one other reason." She got up, walked over to her desk, picked up a picture frame and returned to her chair. "I don't usually share personal information with my patients, but I'm going to tell you something so you don't feel so alone."

Instinctively I sat up. Barbara handed me the frame. The photo was of Barbara with her arm around a younger woman who had a Boston Marathon bib pinned to her shirt. My first instinct was that it was her daughter.

"My girlfriend is twenty years younger than I am," Barbara said. "I know it's not as many as you and Sarah, but we went through those same issues you're fearful of. Some of our friends and family were against it, told us we'd never work out. We've been together almost ten years."

"Really?" A flutter of excitement filled my chest. "What did you say to get them to change their minds?"

Barbara shook her head. "Our goal wasn't to change their minds, only to open them. We told them we loved each other, and that we hoped they could learn to be happy for us. And if not, we'd miss having them in our lives."

I leaned forward and handed the picture back. "Did those family members come around?"

"Most of them, yes." Barbara smiled at the photo before resting it on her lap. "Part of being an adult is about making choices that are right for you, even when others may not agree. It's your life. You need to ask yourself, who do you want to spend it with?"

Joanne pulled up to my apartment. We'd gone to dinner with two couples, friends of hers. I thanked her for a fun evening, and as I reached for the door handle, she handed me a jewelry box. I loved presents but presents from her had strings attached. Inside was a key to her house.

For real?

"If you moved in with me, you could use my second bedroom to write and paint ties," Joanne said. "And you wouldn't have to worry about rent."

"That's a generous offer, but I can't accept."

"Will you at least think about it?" she asked. I nodded, if only to get her to drop it. "So." She touched my thigh. "Can I sleep over?"

"Sorry, not tonight. I have to be at work early." Why was I the one apologizing?

"Why won't you ever let me stay over?" Joanne whined. "I don't take up much room."

She took up more room than she realized.

The second I got out and closed the car door, Joanne sped off, tires squealing. I sighed. I'd thought spending time with her would wean me from Sarah, but love, it turned out, didn't work that way. You couldn't just flick a switch and stop loving one person and start loving another. If anything, the glaring fact of Joanne and I not syncing as a couple made me see how much Sarah and I belonged together—similar interests, good sex, but mostly how I felt just being by her side.

Inside my apartment I had one message on my answering machine. "Blu, come over no matter what time you get home. Linda went to Vermont again."

I ran back out the door.

Twenty minutes later, I walked into Sarah's house. She was in bed reading. I leaned down to kiss her when someone outside leaned on a car horn.

"Who's that?" I asked, startled.

"Kids I bet." Sarah walked over to the window and lifted the shade. I peeked out from the other side. A sedan idled on the street. I tried to decipher the color and make, but it was too dark. After a few more seconds, the car zoomed away.

"Asshole," Sarah said. Then we got into bed and forgot the whole incident.

About a hundred people were gathered in front of Sage Hall, a colonial brick building with a white dome, home to Smith College's music department.

"Go sit with your friends," I told Joanne when the doors opened and the crowd headed inside. "I'll see you after the show."

"I'll wait. There's something I want to tell Sarah."

"What could you possibly want to tell her?" Every nerve ending on my skin was suddenly standing at attention.

"That you're my girlfriend and I'm not intimidated by her like everyone else."

A clenching gripped my insides as I imagined Joanne confronting Sarah. "For starters, Joanne, I'm not your girlfriend. And second, what are you talking about?"

"I followed you." She pointed a finger at me, imitating Uncle Sam in those posters saying, "I Want You."

"When?"

"Last week after I dropped you off. You said you didn't want me to sleep over because you had to be at work early, but then you drove to Sarah's."

A sinking feeling engulfed my already compromised stomach. "That was you honking outside her house?"

"Well, you lied to me." Joanne glared. "I came back to apologize and saw you get into your car. I figured you were going to Sarah's, but I wanted to see for myself."

"I've told you. Sarah and I are still dealing with stuff. Can we please discuss this later?"

"Fine." She stormed away.

Sarah arrived shortly after, tickets in hand. She'd purchased them months ago for herself and Linda, but Linda had gone out of town again, needing to sort more things out.

"You're going to love Kate," Sarah said as we settled into our third-row seats. "She's almost as smart and funny as you."

The lights dimmed, and Sarah took my hand. Comedian Kate Clinton walked to the lectern. Tall and slender, Kate had short, spiky black hair, and looked like a younger version of Sarah.

Eighteen years later, Kate and I would live in the same Manhattan apartment building. The first time I'd seen her was on the elevator. She'd given me her warm signature smile, and my heart had stopped. I'd wanted to say I'd seen her perform years before, how my ex-girlfriend had been a huge fan, but an air bubble of emotion had wedged itself in my throat. Seeing Kate made me think of Sarah, and for a split second my past rushed back as if I was right back in it, as though Sarah were beside me. When the elevator doors opened, I'd mumbled, "Bye." And I'd hurried out before she could see me cry.

~

After the show, Sarah and I cut through clusters of people milling about outside. The residual laughter from Kate's performance and the warm evening air gave an upbeat energy to the summer night.

"Felice!" someone shouted. I turned to see Joanne heading towards us.

"Go," I told Sarah. "I'll catch up."

"Why are you going with *her*?" Joanne said when she reached me, nodding in Sarah's direction. "I thought I was driving you home."

"I found another ride."

"Are you mad at me?"

"No." I was still reeling from the news of her following me to Sarah's house. "Just done. With us."

"Because I followed you?"

"Because I don't like you." I handed Joanne the gold bracelet she'd given me and walked away, quickening my pace to catch up with Sarah.

"Are you in love with Joanne?" Sarah asked when I reached her.

"God, no." And then, not caring about who might see us, I kissed Sarah. I kissed her right there in the middle of Lesbianville, U.S.A.

"I ended it with Joanne." I plopped onto Barbara's couch.

"How do you feel about that?" Barbara shut the door and walked over to her worn leather chair.

"Relieved, but sad." I slipped off my pink sneakers and tucked my feet under me, the hot seat having cooled.

"Why sad? Did you want things to work out with Joanne?" She picked up her notebook.

"No. It's Sarah I want to be with, but I can't, so I need to find someone else, but that's not possible when I'm still in love with her."

"You're always saying you can't be with Sarah, but you are with her, just not in the way you want. Aside from Linda, who may or may not be leaving, what's really standing in your way?"

Tingling tickled my nose. I clenched my teeth and swallowed hard, trying to stop the unavoidable tears. "I know you said to live the life I want, but I keep imagining my parents' reaction. They'd be so disappointed." I stared at my hands fidgeting in my lap.

"That's why it's easier to keep Sarah a secret."

"You're right. Your parents may be disappointed," Barbara said. I looked up at her, shaken to hear her confirm that fear. "But from what you've told me about them, I believe if they knew how happy Sarah made you, they would come around."

Tears blurred my vision.

"When you first came here Felice, you told me the age difference wasn't a problem for you, but I think it is. I think you're projecting your disapproval onto your parents and others because it's easier than facing how you really feel."

I plucked a tissue from the box on the coffee table.

"Felice, if you want to be free from this feeling of shame, you need to allow yourself to be with Sarah one-hundred percent, which includes making it public. Will people have opinions? Yes. But the happiness you'll feel will outweigh this pain."

I wanted to believe her. I wanted to run out of that therapy session, find Sarah and shout, "Let's start a life together!" But my fear was too strong. I didn't have the courage. Not then. Not for a long, long time.

"Twenty-four years ago my water broke," Mom said when she called at 7:00 a.m. "I told Dad it was time to go to the hospital."

"I told her to take a cab," Dad joked on another line. "Happy birthday, sweetheart."

When I left my apartment, there was a giant happy birthday balloon tied to my door handle with a note from Allison. At work, cards and gifts covered my desk. For lunch, instead of our usual dining commons' tuna sandwich, Sarah took me to Judie's for a shared celebration, since her birthday was two days before mine. As we waited for our meals, Sarah handed me a writing journal. Inside the cover she'd written: "Blu. May your 24th and all that follow be as full of life as the last! S."

"Thanks," I said.

"One more gift." Sarah slid the newest edition of the *Women's Traveler* book across the table. I remembered how sad I felt when she'd given me the previous year's copy. Reading my mind, she said, "I thought we would go to one of these places next month."

I ripped off a piece of popover. "How?"

"My aunt is turning ninety in August, and the family is throwing a party in my hometown. I was thinking you could join me, and on the way, we'd stay one night in New Hope." Sarah's foot rested on mine under the table.

"Isn't that something you and Linda would do together?" I looked at her hopeful, but not convinced.

"We don't attend each other's family gatherings."

"Isn't that the point of having a partner? So you don't have to do family stuff alone?"

Sarah lifted her iced tea. "We're old school."

Or just old.

"How could I go with you?"

"We'll say you offered to help with the driving." Sarah had thought this through. I started to cry, unsure whether from happiness at the thought of going away with Sarah or from sadness at the false pretenses. Barbara had said my insistent tears represented my emotional truth trying to get out, and if I wanted the tears to stop, I had two options: declare my love for Sarah or cut things off for good. I decided I could live with the waterworks.

"Happy birthday," Mark said when he called late that night. Allison had just left. She'd brought over pizza and a jigsaw puzzle and we'd listened to music as we'd assembled it. Everything was easy with her, fun, but I didn't have those same butterflies as I did with Sarah. Did relationships need butterflies? At least in the beginning? If lesbian bed death was real, that meant the butterflies eventually flew away, so shouldn't a friendship count for something?

"So," Mark continued, "what's the latest on Days of Our Lesbian Lives?"

"Let's see." I picked up my journal and opened to the last few entries. "In this week's episode, I broke up with Joanne, Linda decided to stay, and Sarah and I are still sneaking around."

"Felice, you do understand this situation isn't fair to you."

"I know."

"What's up with Sarah's job offer? Are you going to take it?"

"Haven't decided."

"Well, don't forget, in New York you've got a freelance writing gig, endless closets to organize, bagels on every corner, and me."

After I hung up with Mark, I wrote in my journal: "A new day, a new beginning, but the same old broken heart."

"Are you okay?" I asked Sarah as we drove to Northampton for dinner. We were celebrating the completion of another successful summer of orientation sessions.

Sarah sighed. "Linda picked a fight today before she left for Vermont. Took me by surprise, that's all."

I checked my rearview mirror and pulled the car over. "Get out. Let's start this evening again."

Taking hold of the door handle Sarah looked back at me. "You're going to leave me, aren't you?"

"On the side of Route 5? I don't think so."

"That's not what I meant." Sarah got out and shut the door.

I rolled down the window. "Hello, stranger. Any interest in a romantic evening?"

"Why yes." Sarah forced a smile.

"Then it's your lucky night. Hop in."

Once Sarah was back in the car, I handed her a red rose I'd planned to surprise her with at dinner. "We might have just met but is it too soon to tell you I love you?"

Sarah's eyes welled up.

"How was the ride?" Mark embraced me after I hopped off the bus at Port Authority in midtown Manhattan.

"Long."

"Hungry?" He took my luggage and grabbed my hand so as not to get separated as he wove between commuters.

"Starving."

"Good. You'll love this new Mediterranean place."

"Is Steven meeting us?" I quickened my pace to keep up with his long strides.

"Yes and no."

"What does that mean?" I yelled over the noise as we exited onto Eighth Avenue. Cars, taxis, buses, and people on 42nd Street were moving every which way. It was mid-August and the humidity enhanced the stench of body odor and street meat.

"I broke up with him."

"When? You didn't tell me."

"You've had your own dating drama." He led me across the street against the walk signal.

"I'm sorry I haven't been there for you." I squeezed his hand. "But wait. You said, 'Yes and no.' Who are we meeting then?"

"Stephen, but with a ph."

"Are all gay guys named Stephen?" I looked up at him, neon lights framing his face.

"Not all." He smiled. "Some are named Mark."

The next evening, we went to Nana T. and Papa's Brooklyn apartment for dinner. After dessert, Papa motioned for me to follow him. "Come. I have another story for the book."

Their den overlooked a small fenced-in backyard that abutted a neighbor's identical backyard. I sat on the couch, pen and paper in hand, and Papa ambled over to his recliner.

"Before the war, I worked at my father's lumber business." Papa leaned back in his chair; his hands folded behind his head. "When the business started losing money, my father suspected his brother, so my job was to watch my uncle."

"Was your uncle stealing money?"

"Yes," Papa said. "And it was my job to get the money back."

It was dark when Mark and I left Brooklyn. As we cruised along parkways, the summer air blowing in, Mark cranked up the soundtrack to *Les Mis*. Singing at the top of our lungs, we crossed the Whitestone Bridge. When Manhattan appeared in the distance, shimmering and enticing, I stared, mesmerized, sure I heard it calling to me, "Come! You can make it here!"

And I smiled, almost trusting I could.

Sarah picked me up the next morning from Mark's, and we headed to Pennsylvania. Cars and trucks whizzed by on the highway as rain pelted the windshield. I should've been euphoric going away with her, but the cloud of infatuation obscuring my judgment for months had evaporated. If Sarah loved me, wouldn't she have broken up with Linda from the start? Wasn't that what a person did when they fell in love with someone else? I believed Sarah when she told me she loved me, yet I also believed her when she said there was no way for us to be together. Why was I so willing to accept our arrangement? Was I more comfortable hiding? Did I not feel deserving of love?

Sarah reached for my hand. I let her take it, surrendering as I'd done countless times to the notion that the only way for us to be together was secretively. I thought of what Barbara had said, that being with Sarah publicly would cancel out my shame. But our situation was different from hers. There hadn't been a "Linda." Too sad to keep thinking about it, I stared out at the road, accepting that a secret love was better than no love.

Aside from the red-and-green sign that read: "Gobbler's Knob: Home of Punxsy Phil. Weather Capital of the World," Punxsutawney, PA, could've been any other rural American town with its mom-and-pop stores surrounding a town square.

"That's where they hold the Phil show." Sarah pointed to a fake tree stump. "And over there." She nodded in the opposite direction. "Is where my father's pharmacy used to be."

Sarah drove out of town, slowing a few miles later in front of a two-story yellow house with a white picket fence saying, "This is where I grew up." From there we drove to the cemetery and left rocks on her parents' headstones.

"Did you ever have a boyfriend?" I asked as we drove back to town.

"In high school. The quarterback of the football team."

"You're joking." I couldn't picture Sarah with a boyfriend, let alone with the top of the high school pecking order.

Sarah raised her three middle fingers, thumb holding down her pinkie. "On my honor."

We checked in to the Pantall Hotel, built in 1888, its threadbare carpeting and worn furniture as old as the structure itself. Dressing for the party, helping each other with zippers and make up, I imagined a life with Sarah, of traveling the world together. It warmed me inside.

"Remember." Sarah slid the room key into her pocket. "Your

reason for coming was to help with the driving."

Just like that, the warmth inside me froze over.

Family and friends filled the hotel's banquet room to celebrate Sarah's Aunt Monabel's ninetieth birthday. Everyone, related or not, called her Aunt Monabel. Photos of Aunt Monabel from every decade of her life were spread around the room, including some with her former music students. Turns out, the piano teacher in the film *Groundhog Day* had been based on her.

As the evening wore on, Sarah's older brother, a broad-shouldered man with a booming voice and a full head of white hair, held court, telling family stories. His tales often had Sarah as the butt of the joke. She might've been a big cheese at UMass, but in Punxsutawney, Sarah was just someone's kid sister.

"Why does everyone call you Sally?" I asked when we walked back to our room.

"That's what everyone called me until I went away to college. Then I insisted on being called Sarah."

I imagined Sarah leaving home all those decades before, young, full of confidence, and ready to take on the world, starting by shedding her nickname.

That night we did not rush, we did not look at the clock, and we did not worry about anyone walking in on us. We fell asleep wrapped in each other's arms, which is how we woke up. And without a word, made love again, as though trying to get as much into our first—and perhaps only—genuine vacation.

We dressed and walked outside. The sun was bright with only a few scattered clouds.

"Great driving weather," Sarah said as we entered the town square. Twenty yards in we stopped in front of an eagle statue carved by Sarah's grandfather. "Before you came into my life, every day was *Groundhog Day*, the same day over and over. But then you appeared, and my world opened. Kiss me, you fool."

"Here? Are you nuts?" I scanned the grounds. A handful of people were seated on benches, some reading newspapers, some staring straight ahead.

"No one knows us."

After we kissed, we returned to the hotel, our pinkies grazing with each step.

Inside the hotel's restaurant, we joined Sarah's brother and his wife, seated by a window, their dishes showing the stains and crumbs of eggs and toast. Her brother, who'd barely shut his mouth the evening before, had a huge smirk on his face. Out the window, the eagle statue stood in perfect view. I felt a pang of humiliation and fear. I glanced at Sarah, guessing she, too, might be embarrassed, but she simply winked at me, found my foot with hers, then opened her menu. She knew he'd seen us and didn't seem to care. In fact, she seemed pleased.

Seven hours later I pulled into the Tanglewood Music Center in Lenox, Massachusetts, eyes bloodshot, back stiff. I'd driven straight from Punxsutawney.

Sarah removed a blanket and two sweatshirts from her trunk. The August air hinted at summer's end. We bought sandwiches and found a spot on the lawn. Waiting for the concert to begin, I told Sarah that my parents had celebrated their engagement here, because my dad had worked in the kitchen during summers when he was in college.

"That makes being here with you so much better." Sarah leaned over to kiss me.

"What are you doing?" I pulled away and glimpsed around at the hordes of people, all eating and drinking, blissful on that dreamlike night with a large moon hanging low.

"No one knows us. And it's James Taylor at Tanglewood. What you wanted."

"But we can't be sure Linda's friends aren't here."

Sarah harrumphed and lay on her back, gazing up at the stars. I wanted nothing more than to lie next to her, but could not get past my apprehension.

"It's official," Sarah said the next morning in bed at our B&B. "Linda's leaving."

"What? When?" I stared at her across the pillow.

"She's been packing while we've been away."

"Why didn't you tell me sooner?"

"I didn't want to spoil our vacation." Sarah traced her hand over my stomach and between my thighs. I relished the sensation she ignited inside me, except this time I had a strange thought: now that Linda no longer wanted to be with Sarah, did I?

After visiting the Norman Rockwell Museum, we returned to Amherst. Sarah dropped me at Milford, promising to call later. I went out that evening with Allison and friends. I told them about Punxsutawney Phil and the James Taylor concert, but nothing of how great it had been to be with Sarah. I couldn't. Only Allison knew about us.

I biked into town early the next morning and dropped off my rent check, still unsure if it was to be my last. I had yet to sign the new lease, which was due in two weeks, before Labor Day. I stopped in Food for Thought and bought a copy of *Entry Level Life: A Complete Guide to Masquerading As a Member of the Real World*, then pedaled home and read it cover to cover. The book was funny and spot on, but it made me disheartened to realize I'd been out of college two years and had yet to make a dent in my goals. My confidence was waning. Was I good enough to be a writer? Or was I only college-level good, like the majority of Division I athletes who never make it to the pros? That's when Sarah's voice appeared in my head. "To accomplish your dream, start now." I grabbed my journal and car keys and bolted out the door.

A half hour later I sat on the back porch of the Montague Bookmill, trying to enjoy the rushing water and chirping birds, but they only made me gloomy. "We'll always have the Bookmill," Sarah had said. But what did we have now besides hidden love letters and journals filled with emotional scars? I'd been so wary of making wrong decisions, but what if I already had? What if moving back to Amherst and being with Sarah *had* been the wrong choice? Resolved it wasn't too late to change course, I ran down the porch steps, picked up a stone, and hurled it into the river. The high holy days were still a month away, but I figured it couldn't hurt to get a jump on my atonement after the year I'd had.

I spent the afternoon in the café editing my grandfather's latest stories about his childhood in Poland before the war. Though not as brutal as his experiences in the labor camps and concentration camps, they did include struggles. As cathartic as it was for him to revisit these experiences, they also reawakened nightmares. But Papa persevered, wanting his children and grandchildren to learn how and why he survived, and I wanted to help him do that. Where it would lead neither of us knew, but we were on that road together.

My office phone rang twice in quick succession, signaling an off-campus call. I snatched it up, hoping it was Sarah. We'd not talked since our return from Punxsutawney the week before. She was still on vacation and dealing with who knows what with Linda.

"I hate to be the bearer of sad news," said Lauren. "The tumor in Tricia's brain won. She died yesterday."

"But she hadn't even lived her dream yet." I pictured Tricia in the newsroom wearing her beat-up leather jacket.

"More proof you need to take advantage of every day."

I walked out of the office, propped open the emergency door, and sat on the top step of the fire escape, staring out at the campus. My gaze settled on the tower library, the tallest library in the United States. Its modern design differed from other buildings on campus, particularly the Old Chapel, UMass's most cherished structure, erected in the late 1800s, squatting in the library's shadow. That was the charm of UMass, its hodgepodge of buildings that stood as testaments to different architectural periods. But now the library was (besides a highlighted square on a kissing map) a symbol of my past. There was a reason we graduated: to move on. But I was holding on for dear life. Why was I so afraid of letting go?

"What are you doing out here?" someone asked. I turned and saw Kimberly. "What's wrong? Why are you crying?"

"A friend died."

"I'm sorry." Kimberly sat beside me. "I came by to tell you I'm moving to Boston. Jen got into grad school at Northeastern."

"That's great." Jealousy rumbled through me. Kimberly's life was moving forward while mine remained a swirl of incomplete and vague commitments.

"Jen got housing, so at least we don't have to worry about rent. What about you? Will you continue working for Sarah?"

I thought of Tricia's brief life and unfulfilled dreams. "No. I'm moving to New York." Hearing it aloud, I knew it was the right decision.

"Thank you for coming," Rachel addressed the six of us—all current UMass employees and former orientation counselors from the last twenty years—sitting around the alumni conference table. "Next summer will be Sarah's twenty-fifth year running the program, and we're planning a surprise reunion. I'd love to hear your stories about her."

Everyone was eager to share. Especially me, but I bit back the urge to talk about the Sarah I knew.

After the meeting, I stayed behind. "Go ahead," I said to Rachel. "I'm sure you've heard the news and are dying to say, 'I told you so.'"

"I would never say that. But let me ask you, after all that's happened, are you going to keep working for Sarah?"

Tears made their uninvited appearance. "That's what I need to talk to you about."

"So," Barbara said during our last scheduled hour before I "graduated" from therapy. "This is it."

"Guess so." I sank into the center of the couch. I would miss the safety of it.

"Will you continue therapy in New York City?"

"Seems a boatload of work, having to start the journey again with someone new."

"True, but you've made some progress and might not want to lose momentum."

"Can I come back if I need a tune-up?"

"My door will always be open. Now, let's see." Barbara flipped back a few pages in her notebook. "At your last appointment we talked about your fears of people knowing you're with Sarah. I've been wondering if that's part of a larger picture." She looked up at me. "You kept Kimberly a secret, and you hid the fact you had a boyfriend in high school. Do you think you're uncomfortable with people knowing you're in a relationship? Or, to be more specific, having sex?"

I squirmed. Barbara noticed my discomfort, but she didn't let up. "Did either of your parents ever talk with you about sex?"

My palms started to sweat. I wiped them on my thighs. "My mom said to wait until marriage."

Barbara bobbed her head slowly, recognizing that impractical but standard advice. "Sex is a tricky area. Few parents talk to their kids about it. And, for sure, kids aren't comfortable asking questions, which often leaves adolescents experimenting and sneaking around with no context for what they're doing. It's normal. But you held onto the secretive aspect. The shame you're feeling may come from the fact that your mother said to wait until marriage, and you didn't. Not about having sex as such, but about disappointing your mother."

"Are you saying this is my mother's fault?" I didn't know whether to laugh or cry.

Barbara shook her head. "No. I'm saying that to avoid the possibility of disappointing your mother, maybe you navigate toward undisclosed relationships. They're your comfort zone."

"More like my discomfort zone." I stared at the floor, too self-conscious to make eye contact.

"The problem with keeping secrets is they can damage our view of ourselves, which it's already showing signs of doing. There's nothing wrong with you for loving Sarah. There will always be people who don't approve of whoever you love, but you can't let them dictate how you feel. The only person you must please is yourself."

I did a last check of my apartment. It was empty except for the shelf unit and the futon, both of which I was leaving for the woman taking over my lease.

"Don't you have soccer practice?" I found Allison leaning against my car, her muscular legs extending out of maroon soccer shorts. Behind us, a young man pushed a lawnmower. The scent of fresh-cut grass was everywhere, a clean, outdoors aroma I'd certainly miss in New York City.

"We had a break, and I wanted to bring you a snack for the ride."

Allison handed me a bag from Bruegger's.

"You are aware New York City is known for their bagels?"

"But do they have your favorite honey grain?" She hugged me and left, promising to keep in touch.

I climbed into the front seat of my car and was adjusting the bags in the back to clear the rear view when a silver sedan pulled up. The door opened and a pair of pink boat shoes, identical to the ones I'd worn on my interview three years earlier, appeared.

"Hi, Blu," Sarah said when I scrambled out. She wore a white polo shirt, khaki shorts, and the green golf belt I'd bought her for her birthday.

I squinted into the mid-morning sun. "How come you haven't called me?"

"I knew it would be easier for you to make a decision."

"Are you upset I didn't take the job?" I hated asking Rachel to break the news, but Sarah had not called me in two weeks, and I feared calling her house.

Sarah smiled, the same warm expression she had when she was holding me in her arms. "I could never be mad at you."

I kicked a pebble and watched it skitter under Sarah's car. "What's happening with Linda?"

"She's moving out next month," Sarah said matter-of-factly.

"What will happen with the cats?"

"The cats will stay with me."

"I'm sorry." I paused. "About everything."

"Blu, listen to me." Sarah cupped my chin in her hand, her touch tender. "You have no reason to be sorry. You're not the reason we split up. If anyone should be sorry, it's me, for dragging you into this mess. Yes, I'm sad Linda's leaving, but I'm sadder that you are." Sarah withdrew her hand. "I've never loved anyone as much as you. I felt this responsibility to be a guide for you, and you were so trusting."

"That's because you made me feel safe. I think the age difference was a plus."

Sarah grinned. "You might be onto something kiddo."

"Sometimes I wondered what you got out of it."

"Blu, you changed my life for the better. I'd do it all again in a heartbeat." Sarah reached into her pocket, removed a brass key charm with six letters engraved on it, along with one shiny key, and handed it to me.

"What's the key for?" I attached it to my UMass alumni key charm.

"My house. As long as I'm there, you'll always have a place to call home. And this too." Sarah removed the BluBlocker sunglasses from atop her head. "Some people look at the world through rose-colored glasses, but orange represents happiness, creativity, and success: everything I hope for you. I look forward to reading all your new experiences."

"Thank you, Sarah." I wrapped my arms around her. It felt like that first hug we'd shared so long ago. As she held me tight, I had a quick thought: with Linda now leaving, there was nothing to stop me from driving to Sarah's house and moving in with her; I'd already packed up my stuff. But no, it was too late. I had made a choice to move to New York City, to pursue a career in writing. I even had a job lined up organizing apartments. Staying would've felt like a cop out. I'd graduated from UMass, and I'd "graduated" from Sarah. It was time to move on. Time to grow up.

"I love you, Blu. I'll always love you."

"I love you, too." We split apart, and I got into my car.

Sarah rested her arms on the open window ledge, the gold cat charm resting in the hollow of her neck. "Remember." She reached in and placed her hand over my heart. "I'm still there." Then, her tone shifting into boss mode, she said, "You are aware New York City drivers are worse than Happy Valley ones?"

"Yes." I put on the BluBlockers.

"Well, in case you forget, you've got your reminder." Sarah nodded to the key charm. The letters WOFTOG glimmered in the sun. Sarah leaned in and kissed me. I tasted salt from her tears. Or were they from mine? She pulled back and caressed my cheek. The imprint of her touch lingered as I drove away. Watching her wave in the rearview mirror, it dawned on me. In all the time Sarah had been telling me to watch out for the other guy—meaning to keep my eye out for anyone who might drive me off the road—never once had it occurred to me that the other guy might've been me.

I was the one who, in my car the year before, had decided to change course and instead of going to New York City, had chosen to go to Amherst to see Sarah. Had I intentionally gone back to avoid having to venture out on my own? I'd thought of Amherst as a protective bubble. In my time there I'd been a student and an employee, and everything had felt safe. Maybe that's why I'd never quite believed our affair was real: because it took place in this fantasy location.

But I'd been wrong. The relationship was real. People had gotten hurt. I'd gotten hurt. All that time I thought I'd been putting off the real world when in fact I'd been knee deep in it. Being an adult, I'd learned, was not only about paying rent and having a job. It was also about the decisions you made. And I had been making bad ones. But being an adult also meant learning from your mistakes.

Deciding to leave Amherst, to leave Sarah, wasn't easy, but I thought of the thousands of new students who'd come to UMass—scared and intimidated—and had persevered, as I'd done only a few years before. Going to New York City would be no different—a small fish venturing into a larger pond. Looking at all that I'd accomplished here, I was sure I could do it again there.

I Got This!
September 1994–November 4, 2002

After six months in the Big Apple, I considered moving back to Amherst. Ben's editor liked the pieces I'd submitted but had yet to publish any. I'd assumed once I'd arrived, everything would fall into place: a writing job, a cool loft apartment, and loads of friends. That wasn't the case. Not even close. For starters, I slept on a twin bed in the corner of my uncle's bedroom in his Bronx apartment. But I couldn't complain. The rent fit my budget: free. The organizing company I worked for paid me $15 an hour while billing the client $150 an hour. Mark called my boss my "pimp." I'd organized the closets of a Broadway producer, a national morning-show TV host, a rock star, and a supermodel with racks of clothing in every room. Even though I loved uncluttering people's lives and turning their chaos into order, I would return home too exhausted to write. I felt I was falling behind. My college friends seemed to be thriving. Lauren was an editor at a local newspaper, her husband Charlie was a VP in some accounting firm, and they'd bought a house. I couldn't even afford my own studio apartment.

To cope, I called Sarah two, sometimes three times a day. She reminded me that becoming a writer wasn't going to happen overnight, and that I had to stick with it. She also said her job offer remained. I was tempted, but Mark persuaded me to give the city at least one year. He was right. I might have been lonely and miserable, but I owed it to myself to try. That didn't mean I couldn't visit Sarah.

During those monthly weekend visits we went to movies, shopped for bargains at TJ Maxx, and slept in the same bed, agreeing to keep it platonic. Until one night Sarah reached for me, her fingers picking up where they'd left off, as though reopening a book she'd stopped reading.

"I don't think we should," I said. In that instant, the spark in Sarah's eyes, the one that filled me with comfort and assured me everything would be okay, extinguished, and with it any sense of security I had in the world. So, I kissed her back. The sparkle in her eye soon returned, conveying that I was the only thing that mattered. I would leave those visits confused. Were we back together? Was I using Sarah as a crutch? We didn't tell anyone. Not because of Linda, who had moved to another state to live with a former girlfriend, but because we knew no other way.

In April, as the buds on the trees in Van Cortlandt Park began to blossom, a childhood friend invited me to London where she taught elementary school. With no day-to-day commitments, I filled a backpack, grabbed my passport, and off I went.

I saw Piccadilly Circus, Buckingham Palace, and Westminster Abbey. After two days, I hugged my friend goodbye and took the Chunnel train to Paris. I toured museums, strolled gardens, and subsisted on baguettes and fruit I bought on the street, getting by with what I remembered from my three years of high school French.

After four days I boarded a train for Barcelona, then on to Nice, Florence, and Venice, spending a few days in each, sleeping in youth hostels, befriending strangers, and writing in my journal. Those two weeks by myself, figuring out train schedules in foreign languages and exploring cities by foot, proved to me I could make it in New York. I came home determined to do just that.

As I'd done after Josh broke up with me, I got busy. I woke early and wrote before work. I took a second job organizing pharmaceutical events around the country, and I enrolled in a television-production course. In that course I met a woman who introduced me to the social scene in Park Slope, a slice of Brooklyn known for tree-lined streets, historic brownstones, and lesbians.

Early one Saturday morning in May, I drove to Brooklyn to try out for the Prospect Park Women's Softball League. Only one other woman was at the field, and she was holding a baseball glove.

"Hi." I approached her. "This is probably an obvious question, but are you here for tryouts?"

"Yes." Her eyes looked almost as dark as her short hair, the ends of which poked out from beneath her Yankees baseball hat. "I'm early."

"Better ten minutes early than one minute late."

"So true," she said. "And I came all the way from the Bronx."

"Me too."

She smiled. "Where in the Bronx?"

"Near Riverdale. I moved there last fall. I'm from Cape Cod."

"You grew up on Cape Cod?" Her voice ticked up an octave. "I go to Provincetown every summer." Was the mention of Provincetown a telltale sign of gayness? Never mind. We were at softball tryouts. Softball was the telltale sign. "I'm Dana." She reached out her hand.

"Felice," I said, shaking it. "What do you do?"

"Cop. You?"

"Writer. Well, I want to be a writer. For now, I'm an organizer."

"With unions?"

"No," I said. "With closets."

A half hour later the field was filled with women; tryouts were underway. After I caught fly balls in the outfield, the coaches called me in to hit.

"Good job out there." Dana came over to me when I'd finished knocking a few balls up the middle. "I coach a fast-pitch team in Manhattan and we need an outfielder. We play on weekends, so it won't interfere with this league. Interested?"

"I go out of town some weekends."

"That's okay." Dana handed me a slip of paper with her cell phone number on it, her fingers skimming mine. "Think about it."

"Honey, who's this?" A woman in a flowery dress draped her arms around Dana.

"Hi, I'm Felice." I reached out my hand, but the woman just

looked down her nose at me. Dana looked mortified as she explained I was new to the area. I said it was nice meeting them both, gathered my stuff and left. I was almost to my car on the outskirts of the park when someone called my name.

"Sorry about that." Dana jogged up to me.

"About what?" I tried to ignore a recognizable tingling in my stomach.

"My girlfriend and I moved in together last weekend and—"

"That's great." I cut her off.

"No, it's not."

"Why?" I asked.

"Because I think I just fell in love with someone else."

My affair with Dana followed the same playbook as my affair with Sarah: secrets, lies, and plenty of make-out sessions in her car. I wasn't sure if I was attracted to Dana or to the drama that came along with the affair. As Barbara said, it was my comfort zone.

As spring turned into summer, Dana and I played softball together a few times a week in Brooklyn and Manhattan. She drove me home after every practice and game, the two of us cruising over the Brooklyn Bridge and up the FDR holding hands and listening to Rush or U2, her favorite bands, hoping for traffic to prolong our time together. Occasionally her girlfriend would come to a game and on the ride home, I'd sit in the backseat, Dana and I stealing glances through her rearview mirror.

Our affair excited me, but with it came obvious obstacles—for instance, I couldn't call when her girlfriend was home. This triggered memories of when I'd wanted to call Sarah just to say goodnight, and couldn't because Linda was there. As hard as this familiar scenario was, on some strange level it was also reassuring. I knew my role and accepted the circumstances without question.

Dana was a few years older than I, a few credits shy of a college degree, and when in uniform, she was serious and focused. But off the clock? The kindest, gentlest person I'd ever met. And could she tell a story. From chasing perps in run-down Bronx neighborhoods to the time she pulled out a gun in an apartment full of cat-sized rats, she kept listeners' attention.

Mark liked Dana but was against the affair, reminding me of

what had happened with Sarah. I explained it was different this time. That Dana had offered to break up with her girlfriend to be with me, but I'd told her no. I wasn't comfortable playing that role. Other woman? More my style.

Ten months into the affair, Dana's girlfriend got wind of the situation and moved out. I packed up my stuff. Mark said to make sure I was ready to take the relationship with Dana to the next level. I dismissed his warning, saying the move was solely prudent, for in New York City, couples shacked up sooner because rents are expensive. And while money was a factor, I also hoped the move would wean me off Sarah, break my dependence on her, and allow me to be committed to Dana.

Our bright one-bedroom apartment in Throggs Neck, a strip of the Bronx full of semi-attached homes along the East River, reminded me of Cape Cod, with its numerous marinas and seafood restaurants. Dana and I bought monogramed bath towels, hosted parties, and even got a parakeet.

Several months after moving in together, Dana suggested we become domestic partners. To me it meant health benefits. To Dana, it meant commitment. We went to the City Clerk's Office in downtown Manhattan, handed over the required paperwork, paid the fee, and left, certificate in hand. Outside, Dana suggested we sit for a minute. We found a bench in a small park, and, serenaded by the sound of traffic entering the Brooklyn Bridge, Dana presented me with a gold wedding band. I didn't know how to respond so I just slid it on the ring finger of my right hand.

"I think you're supposed to wear it on the left hand," Dana said. But there was already a ring there, the silver band Sarah had given me in Provincetown. I swapped the rings and began to tear up. Dana thought it was from happiness. It wasn't. I was not in love with her. How could I be when Sarah still occupied that space in my heart?

Meanwhile, my daily calls to Sarah continued, as did my monthly visits. I told Dana that Sarah was like my family and needed my help around the house. Which was true. After Linda had moved out, I had reorganized every closet and cabinet in Sarah's house, filling the empty spaces where Linda's stuff had been. Some of the spaces I'd even filled with my own stuff. I helped her with house tasks that Linda used to do, like raking leaves and sealing windows before the winter. Sarah had been sad after Linda left, and I still blamed myself for their breakup, which is why when Sarah asked me to visit, I always said yes. But it wasn't solely guilt that kept me coming back. I still felt at home by her side.

I would return to New York after those visits feeling guilty, wondering how Sarah had been able to cheat on Linda all those times. Eventually, those visits began to eat at me. I felt torn in two directions. Sarah couldn't wait to see me, and Dana hated to see me go. That arrangement went on for years, until around the time I had a chance encounter with a magazine editor whose apartment I had been hired to organize. While knee deep in a pile of his clothes, he told me about his friend starting a women's basketball magazine who was looking for writers. Basketball and writing? My heart had almost jumped out of my chest.

On a warm April evening in midtown Manhattan, I entered the Four Seasons Hotel, my heels clicking against the marble tiles. I sat in the swanky lobby across from a Pulitzer Prize-winning journalist from the *New York Daily News.* Wendy wore a crisp navy suit, her hair pulled back exposing diamond studs that didn't twinkle half as brightly as her eyes, a reflection of her enthusiasm as she spoke about *Women Next,* her innovative women's basketball magazine.

"You've got great energy and you're funny," Wendy said. "I'd love to work with you." It would be a year, however, until the funding came through, and she suggested I apply to be an assistant editor at the *Daily News.* "We could start working on the first issue until then."

I walked out of the Four Seasons and called Sarah on my cell phone, the first person with whom I always wanted to share my good news. But it was hard to hear her. Not because of the taxis and buses screeching along 57th Street, but because Sarah's voice sounded strained.

"There's something I need to tell you, Blu." Sarah paused. "I've got cancer."

I froze on the sidewalk. Someone muttered, "Asshole" as they walked around me.

"My doctor found a lump in the lining of my stomach."

"Is he sure it's not a doughnut? You ate that entire box of Krispy Kremes I brought you last weekend." Humor kicking in to deflect my real emotions.

"I wish. The doctor wants to remove it. I'm scheduled for an operation next week."

"That's good, isn't it? He'll take it out and then you'll be fine?" My feet started to move again. I turned up 8th Avenue toward Columbus Circle.

"I hope so. But to avoid surprises, I want your help writing my will. I want you to have the house."

"I'd rather have you not die."

"I'm not going to die," Sarah said. "It's just a precaution. My house is as much yours as mine. I'd never want you to lose that."

Two days later I interviewed with the *Daily News* editor who looked up from my resume and said, "You're overqualified." I explained to him I wanted to get my foot in the door to be a writer, and he explained that the woman I was replacing was too busy to write. I said I'd write on my own time.

"Do you think this scar is ugly?" Sarah lifted her shirt to reveal the five-inch vertical wound, still puffy and pink, racing up her abdomen. It had been a week since the doctor had removed her tumor, and I'd come to help with recovery. My new boss at the *Daily News* had allowed me to postpone my start for a week.

"No," I said. "But you can kiss goodbye that bikini modeling career you'd always wanted."

Sarah shot me a tired grin. "Bite me."

It was three in the morning, and we were sitting on her bathroom floor. Sarah had had the urge to move her bowels, but so far, false alarms. And since she found it too much effort to walk back and forth to the bathroom, she'd stayed put. I kept her company.

"What do you say I give you a tattoo?" I ripped open a rub-on tattoo I'd brought as part of my "other duties as assigned" to make cancer funny, and placed it alongside her scar. After dabbing the back with a damp tissue, I peeled off the plastic. Sarah looked down at the fierce dragon whose pointy tail crisscrossed up from her pubic bone to her belly button.

"The doctor will shit when he sees this tomorrow," Sarah said.

"At least one of you will."

"Ow." Sarah placed her hand over her stomach. "Don't make me laugh."

"But Chemo-Sabe, you said that was my job."

"You're right." Sarah smiled at her new nickname. "Keep it up."

During my first week at the *Daily News*, aside from answering phones, opening mail, paying bills, and typing "Voice of the People" letters, I created a filing system for the editorial board, organized office supplies (as well as my boss's desk), and still had time to write.

That first Friday afternoon, an hour before heading home, I walked into the op-ed editor's office and handed him an opinion piece I'd written about my grandmother's suicide, the result of her experiences in the Holocaust. His wild gray eyebrows shot up, either from shock at my fearlessness or impressed. He promised to read it, and I returned to my desk.

Minutes later he came out of his office. "This is good," he told me. "I'm going to run it tomorrow."

That year, aside from writing more op-eds, meeting Vice President Al Gore, First Lady Hillary Clinton, and US Senator John McCain (all of whom were running for office in 2000 and wanted the endorsement of the *Daily News'* editorial board), I had a brief fling with a male coworker. He and I bonded over each of us having a loved one battling cancer.

Greg was in his mid-thirties, separated from his wife, and had a young daughter. The sex was my idea. I had wanted to take another stab at sleeping with men before I turned thirty, and he was willing to assist in my research. Turns out, I enjoyed sex with him. More so than with Dana. Not ready to deal with this revelation, I decided to do as I always did: record the details in my journal and keep my mouth shut.

In June, a month before the launch of *Women Next,* I attended a WNBA New York Liberty basketball game at Madison Square

Garden. My job was to stand behind a table and sign up subscribers as I had when I'd been the green dean, except the product then was UMass.

During the last quarter, Dana showed up, eyes on fire. She had read my journal. Standing in a stairwell amid the aroma of popcorn and the deafening sound of cheering girls, I did my best to explain I'd only slept with Greg to rule out if I liked sleeping with men.

"And do you?" Dana asked. "Like sleeping with men?"

"No," I lied. What girlfriend wants to hear otherwise?

I spent weeks apologizing, and things went back to normal. But I should've taken that incident as an opportunity to break up with Dana. Had I started that affair because I'd wanted to be caught? Because it was easier than doing the grown-up thing of ending the relationship? Was I still following Sarah's lead?

I gave notice in July at the *Daily News*, set up my new office in the magazine's downtown loft, turned thirty, and flew to Arizona to cover the WNBA All-Star Game. My responsibilities—writing articles, organizing media and giveaway events, signing up subscribers, hobnobbing in locker rooms alongside sportscasters like Robin Roberts, and interviewing WNBA players—was the culmination of every job I'd ever had, my past a steppingstone to this moment. Buoyed by confidence, I decided to break up with Dana. But before I had the chance, the dotcom crash hit, the magazine shuttered, and the shaky ground beneath my feet kept me from making any sudden moves.

"It feels like a chickadee." I rubbed Sarah's bare scalp. It was spring 2001, two years since her surgery and her peach-fuzz hair had been taking its sweet time growing back. We were sitting on the couch in her living room, reading the newspaper.

"I have to reschedule next month's visit," Sarah said.

"Why?" I stopped rubbing her head.

Sarah rested the paper on her lap and removed her reading glasses. "I started dating someone. We're going to Florida."

A wave of nausea coursed through me. "Does this mean you don't love me anymore?" I knew my reaction was selfish. Sarah deserved to be happy, and I had, after all, been living with Dana for years, but the thought of her looking at someone else the way she looked at me made me queasy.

"Blu, of course I still love you. This is about me being lonely." Sarah moved aside the newspaper and opened her arms. I nestled into her and she pressed her hand against my chest above my heart. "I promise I'll always still be there."

"What the hell was that?" Dana, newly promoted to sergeant, was at One Police Plaza in downtown Manhattan. She had called to wish me luck before I headed into the city for a job interview at Hunter College. "Our building just shook. I'll call you back." Seconds later she did. "A plane hit the World Trade Center. Don't know the details. Will call when I can."

I put on the TV. Every channel aired the image of smoke billowing out of the North Tower. I stared at the screen in disbelief until the unthinkable happened: a second plane rammed into the South Tower. I sprinted down the street to the East River. Standing with neighbors in the shadow of the Throggs Neck Bridge, I gazed at the Manhattan skyline as a trail of smoke traveled from the tip of the financial district into Brooklyn.

Soon one tower crumbled like a sandcastle, sending a huge plume billowing up into the cloudless sky. It looked unreal, like watching a movie. Around me were gasps. Screams. Time seemed frozen. Were there people in the building? On the plane? On the ground? I knew there had to be, but the fact that they were dying as we stood watching was too surreal to comprehend. I ran home and called Dana.

"Terrorists," she said. "Not sure when I'll get home."

Two weeks after two planes knocked down the twin towers, I went on that interview I'd had planned the morning of 9/11. The president of Hunter College, who also happened to be the wife of my former boss at the *Daily News,* said to me, "After how you organized the office at the *News*, I want you to come run mine."

At thirty-one I became her chief of staff. Challenging wasn't the half of it. Aside from overseeing a team of five, I hired three student workers, laughing to myself when I told them, "Better ten minutes early than one minute late." I sat on numerous committees, and operated as the president's liaison to vice presidents, administrators, faculty, students, and alumni. I loved the job, but it didn't take long for the stress to take its toll. A friend in my spin class suggested yoga. But yoga didn't match my pace. Yoga meant slow.

"Just try it," he said. "The instructor's great." The class was right after my 6 a.m. spin, so I figured what the heck, I was already there.

Erin, the yoga instructor, was in her early forties, tall and sinewy. Her arms resembled ropes; each muscle had a muscle. She wore black tights, a pink tank top, and her dirty-blonde hair was pulled back into a high, sleek ponytail.

"Is this anyone's first class?" Erin asked the two dozen men and women seated cross-legged on purple mats. My hand shot up as if I were a teacher's pet in a third-grade classroom. "Welcome." Erin smiled at me. "Do what you can. I'll be around to help." Then she dimmed the lights and turned on the music. Kenny Loggins began to sing. Kenny in yoga? My reservations about yoga waned.

While I practiced my first downward dog, Erin placed her hands on my hips and lifted them higher. It reminded me of the first time I'd played golf with Sarah, when she'd corrected my grip on the club. But in the yoga studio it was customary to do adjustments. As my body settled into the stretch, the persistent pain in my lower back disappeared for the first time in years.

"That was amazing," I said to Erin after class.

"Thanks." She tucked her rolled-up mat under her well-developed arm.

"How often do you teach it?"

"Every morning," she said.

I returned the next morning. And the next. Erin's hands-on instruction continued.

A month later, Erin announced she was hosting a yoga and meditation workshop in Westchester that upcoming Sunday.

"Think you can come?" Erin asked when I picked up a flier.

"Yes." I had plenty of alone time then, as Dana worked most weekends assisting families of 9/11 victims.

"Great." She patted my arm, sending a rippling through to my stomach.

~

The workshop was held in a warm wood-paneled room at a community center in Dobbs Ferry, a river town north of Manhattan. There were about thirty people, of all ages and sizes. We started with chanting and breathing. I found myself swept up in the moment, feeling as though all those years of practicing Barbara's calming technique had prepared me for that day.

The class ended before noon. I was putting on my sneakers when Erin squatted beside me. "I'm heading to Bear Mountain to go for a hike. Want to come?"

On the climb up, we shared stories of how we'd wound up in New York City. Erin had grown up near Albany, had graduated from business school, and had worked for fifteen stressful years at a hedge fund on Wall Street. Having saved a lot of money, she'd quit her job and pursued her passion: yoga.

At the summit we sat on a rock, soaking in the magnificent view of the rolling mountains, with the Manhattan skyline a hazy, serrated image in the distance.

"I hike every Sunday." Erin removed a turkey sandwich from her backpack and split it with me. "Let me know if you ever want to tag along."

The next weekend we hiked The Gunks in New Paltz, and Breakneck Ridge in Cold Spring after that. Almost every Sunday for the next few months we hiked somewhere new. Sometimes I packed the sandwiches.

One cold Sunday in January, after our hike, Erin invited me to her place for dinner. Her spacious one-bedroom condo, decorated in earth tones, overlooked the New Jersey Palisades along the Hudson River. As the sun slipped behind the steep mountain cliffs, I confessed to Erin I had a crush on her. To my delight, she reciprocated.

Ending things with Dana wasn't easy. I finally understood why Sarah hadn't wanted to hurt Linda all those years before, but I knew it was crueler to stay.

On the night of Valentine's Day, I arrived home late from another long workday to find lit candles spread around the living room, a vase of roses on the coffee table, and, beside it, a gift-wrapped present. Guilt ate at me, knowing the words on my tongue would soon obliterate the romantic setting Dana had created.

I moved back in with my uncle into a new two-bedroom apartment in his same building. I was sad about leaving Dana but knew it had been the right move for us both. I'd never been fully committed to her. How could I when I had still been tied to Sarah? But now Sarah had a new girlfriend, and I felt free to move on without restrictions.

"Welcome to the Montague Bookmill," I told Erin as we descended the back staircase, the Sawmill River running below. A new restaurant, the Blue Heron, had opened there. The name "Blue" was not lost on me.

"Felice, is that you?" Connie approached with the aid of a cane. Behind her, Nan glowered. Rachel and a few others came over, and I introduced them to Erin. When Sarah and Katherine arrived, everyone yelled, "Surprise!"

As I waited for my turn to wish Sarah a happy birthday, I inspected Katherine. She was Sarah's age, had dark-red hair, a bright smile, and held tight to Sarah's hand. In the year she and Sarah had been dating, we'd never met. Whenever I had visited Sarah, Katherine had stayed at her own place. Now, watching the two of them, I felt happy for Sarah. She had found someone. As had I. Time and distance had allowed us to meet new people, let go, and move on.

"Happy birthday, Sarah." I hugged her, shocked by how frail she felt. It had been two months since my last visit, the longest we'd ever gone without laying eyes on each other. Her hair had grown back more, but the color was lighter, almost translucent.

"Felice, so nice to see you." Sarah hadn't said my actual name in almost a decade. It sounded wrong.

"Sarah, I'd like you to meet Erin, my new girlfriend."

"I've heard so much about you," Erin said. "Felice talks about you all the time."

"I wish I could say the same." Sarah shot me a look. She was irritated, although the others would've read this as humorous.

"How long have you two been together?"

"Five months." Erin put her arm around my waist. Sarah's eyes followed, her brow wrinkling. She hated surprises.

Our party was seated around a rustic table with a view of the river. As the women read the menu, Erin leaned close, whispered, "Thanks for bringing me," and kissed me. I glanced up. Sarah was looking at me over the top of her reading glasses. I felt the old flutter of attraction despite her dour expression.

Sarah pushed her chair back and walked out. I waited a beat, then excused myself, saying I needed to use the restroom.

Entering the adjacent bookstore, I walked up the curved staircase and found the birthday girl staring out a window at the water that harbored our thrown stones from long ago. I rested my chin on Sarah's shoulder.

"You two look happy together, Blu," Sarah said without looking back.

"We are."

"Do you remember what I told you the first time I brought you here?"

"That we'll always have the Bookmill."

"Well." Sarah turned and took my face in her hands. "We always will." Then she pressed her lips to mine.

I pulled back. "What are you, nuts?"

Sarah sighed. "Forget cancer, seeing you with Erin is killing me."

"What are you saying? You said you were happy with Katherine."

"I am, but you're the one I'm in love with. Always have been. My biggest regret is not having given us an actual chance."

So much for her moving on.

"Sarah, where is this coming from?" I sensed myself coming unglued.

"My cancer's back."

"How? The doctor said you were in remission."

"I started taking estrogen replacement again. It increased my cancer cell count."

"Did the doctor tell you to take it? We can get a lawyer. We can sue." A to-do list began forming in my head.

"No." Sarah shook her head. "It was a boneheaded decision on my part. Thought it would help."

"Well, chemo worked once. Maybe it will again."

"It's too late." Faint beads of sweat dotted Sarah's upper lip. "My doctor said I have six months, and I want to spend as much of that time as I can with you." She kissed me again. I was no longer interested in her in that way, but our past drew me right back under her spell.

The next few months were a blur. I visited Sarah often, using up vacation days and calling in sick. Sarah explained to Katherine I was preparing the house for when she'd no longer be there. I told Erin the same thing. And while I was cleaning out closets and filling boxes for donation, Sarah directing from a club chair, blanket tucked around her, cat on her lap, we were also living the life we'd dreamed of: evenings spent reading the paper, piano music on the stereo, dinner cooking on the stove, cats wandering about. The sexual urge we'd once had to connect had simply become the urge to be together. Would this have been my life had we tried to make a go of it and I'd never gone to New York? Would I have gotten over the age difference? Would family and friends have accepted our relationship? Would we have proven that age didn't factor in when it came to love? Or would we have fizzled out, realizing that it did? All these years later, it no longer matters to me if we had or hadn't worked out. At least we would've done what we'd wanted instead of doing what we thought we should. I thought we should keep our situation classified to avoid disappointing my parents, and Sarah thought she should stay with Linda out of obligation. In the end, by keeping our affair under wraps, I remained half connected to Sarah, half connected to who I was, and half connected to who I could be.

Late one Sunday afternoon, Sarah and I were sitting in the hot tub in her backyard, her face ghostlike with condensation. The sun was low, and a few remaining orange leaves danced in the late-October breeze.

"I'm leaving the house to Katherine," Sarah said out of nowhere, in a casual voice, as though taking away what she'd promised me was no big deal.

"Did you forget you said I'd always have your house to come home to?" A whimper rose inside me like the bubbles popping to the surface of the tub. It seemed "always" now had a termination date, one more imminent with each passing second. The idea of losing Sarah, of no longer having her in my life, frightened me. Not that a house could've replaced that loss, but I'd begun to think of her house as an extension of her. Our last connection. The house was filled with our memories, laughter, tears, love. "Why did you change your mind?"

Sarah leaned her head back against an inflatable cushion. "Your life's in New York. Plus, there are the boys. I can't move them. This is their home too." Was she really leaving Katherine the house because of cats or because it was more appropriate to give the house to someone closer in age, thereby dispelling long-standing rumors about us? "What if I tell Katherine to leave it to you?"

"As if that'll happen. Katherine thinks I'm just a former employee of yours. She doesn't know the truth. Perhaps I should tell her what's been going on these past few months."

Sarah lifted her head off the pillow, her chin dipping beneath the water's surface. "You promised you wouldn't."

"You're right. At least one of us should keep her promises."

"Do you want my Volkswagen?"

"No. My grandparents are Holocaust survivors. I can't drive a German car."

"Then what do you want?" Sarah looked tired. My whining wasn't helping.

"Proof that you love me." My fingertips felt tight, the skin had started to prune.

"Blu, just because I'm giving the house to Katherine doesn't mean I don't love you. We'll always be soulmates. The cats need to be taken care of, and you're in New York. I feel bad enough I won't be here for them."

"What about me?" I wanted to shout. Instead, I kept quiet and stepped out of the tub into faint slivers of sunlight slipping between bare tree limbs and wrapped myself in a terrycloth bathrobe. Sarah got out, forgoing her robe as she struggled to lift the heavy cover, her arms and legs jiggling. Chemotherapy had eaten away her muscles.

"Let me help you." I reached for the other end and my bathrobe opened.

"I can do it." Sarah's voice was adamant. I let go, amazed at her determination. After securing the cover, Sarah tied a robe around her emaciated frame and stepped toward me, her expression softening as she swiped her fingertips against my exposed breast. For the briefest of moments, a sweetness of past days flickered between us.

"Sarah, you've got to get rid of some turtlenecks." I dropped a stack onto the bed next to her. She'd felt dizzy after our dip in the hot tub and had needed to rest.

"But I might need—" Sarah squeezed her eyes shut, agony in her features as she placed her hands over her stomach.

"Should I get your pain meds?"

She groaned. "The meds are useless."

"Maybe you should sleep. I can switch your summer and winter clothes later."

"I'll sleep enough when I'm dead." Sarah pulled the hood of her gray Cape Cod sweatshirt over her head. "Switching my clothes is a helpful distraction." She picked up a hardcover book from her nightstand and tossed it across the bed. "I got this for you. It's about a girl who's killed by a neighbor. It's excellent."

"Oh, yeah, sounds it." I picked up the copy of *The Lovely Bones*.

"Well, smartass, what makes it compelling is that it's told from the dead girl's perspective as she watches her family heal and comes to terms with her own death."

I cracked open the cover and read: "Hey, Blu. Watch out, I'll be watching you. Love, Sarah." Slipping the book into my overnight bag, I walked into the closet so Sarah wouldn't see me wipe away tears.

"I forgot to tell you about the coffee enema I had last week," Sarah said as I placed a pile of sweaters onto the bed for her to inspect. It toppled onto Kenny, Sarah's newest cat, who slunk over to a spot beside Sarah. "I had to kneel over a table, naked from the waist down, while this woman slipped a tube up my rear end. In no time my body filled with coffee."

"Decaf?" I stuffed old turtlenecks into a giveaway bag.

"Forgot to ask." Sarah ran her hand over Kenny's pale-orange head. He squeezed his eyes closed and purred. "When my stomach expanded, I got nervous. The woman kept telling me to relax and breathe."

"I'm sure that's easy to do when Maxwell House is pumping through your ass."

"I told her I was doing my best, but that it's difficult to breathe during such an intimate encounter."

"Now do you understand why you always had to remind me to breathe during our intimate encounters?" I said. Sarah smiled, but her face soon drained of color as she brought her hands back to her stomach. I ran to her side. "Sarah, what can I do?"

She forced a weak smile. "How about a poke in the eye with a sharp stick?"

I left Sarah's the next morning—her waving from the front steps, me waving from my car, both of us with tears streaming down our cheeks. Goodbyes were the hardest: not knowing if Sarah's cancer would keep us from sharing more time together. I returned to the Bronx and fell into my uncle's arms. Mark was the only one who knew what those visits meant.

The next night, my phone rang. I'd been sitting in my room, editing my grandfather's book. Mark was cooking dinner and the apartment smelled of roasted chicken. I glanced out my bedroom window at the trees lining Van Cortlandt Park, a creamy pink sunset just beyond, and picked up the phone. "Hi, Rachel. What's up?"

"Something's happened. Sarah's in—"

"The hospital, I know," I cut her off. "She called me after she got there this morning. Said the doctor wanted to do some tests. She said she was fine."

"She's not fine," Rachel said. "She's in a coma."

"And last, but not least, to my brother-in-law, Louie, who always said I'd never remember him in my will. Hello, Louie!" I nailed the punch line, but Sarah didn't react. "Come on, Sarah. You love this joke." I held her lifeless hand, hoping she'd recognize my voice and squeeze, but not a muscle stirred. I took a yellow Discman from my bag, put the headphones on Sarah's head, and hit play. As Kenny Loggins sang "Only A Miracle," Sarah's eyes zoomed back and forth behind her eyelids. Was her brain registering the song? Would she wake up? When the music faded, Sarah's eyelids ceased moving.

I removed the headphones and put the Discman on the nightstand alongside a John Grisham thriller and a tube of ChapStick, last-minute items Sarah had taken with her to the hospital when she thought she'd be waiting around to see the doctor.

"Time to go," said a nurse with a Jamaican accent. "Visa'ting hours be ovah."

I leaned close to Sarah. "I love you," I said, then walked out, not wanting to believe this was the last time I'd ever see her.

For five days I waited for the call from Rachel to say that Sarah had died. My phone never left my side. I slept with it under my pillow, took it in the shower, and even rode the bus instead of the subway since underground had no reception. Nothing was going to keep me from answering.

Well, almost nothing.

On Saturday morning I was sitting in a synagogue at my cousin's bar mitzvah when the call finally came. I wanted to answer. I needed to hear "Sarah's dead" for it to be real. But that wasn't possible. As the call went to voicemail, my cousin's voice cracked on the words, "Abraham had lost his beloved wife, Sarah." I jerked my head up. Sarah? What were the odds? My chest constricted. I closed my eyes and breathed slowly through my nose. In, out. In, out.

"You okay?" Uncle Mark whispered.

"I just got the call," I whispered back. "I need to leave."

"But you're expected up there. You promised Adam."

That morning, Adam, adorable in his suit and tie, chin dusted with acne, had asked me to perform the ritual of lifting the Torah. I'd agreed, but now? A familiar voice appeared in my head. "Suck it up." Sarah's tart response whenever a critical task was on the line. She'd want me to do it.

The rabbi nodded at me from the podium. My cue. I stood and

squeezed by Jackie, who tucked a few strands of long hair behind her ear, flashing her engagement ring as she mouthed, "Don't drop it." Next, Meredith, now taller than I was, smirked as she pinched my rear end. Seeing the sadness in my eyes she'd only wanted to cheer me up.

When I passed my father, he patted my back—his signature "Go get 'em" gesture, as if I were stepping up to bat with the bases loaded. My mother and Nana T. both kissed my cheek, each leaving lipstick stains I only became aware of when Papa wiped them away with his hefty thumb.

I walked onto the bimah, the stares of the two hundred guests watching me. Feeling in closer proximity to God, I silently asked, Why did you let Sarah get cancer? No answer.

On the podium I wound my fingers around the Torah's smooth wooden handles and stared at the columns of ancient script as I raised it above my head. My arm muscles quaked. That ancient scroll was heavy with history. Slowly, I turned in a circle, allowing the congregation to see the yellowed parchment paper filled with words of wisdom. I thought of Sarah's own wisdom, which she'd been handing down to me for years.

"How're you doing?" asked the rabbi, concerned I might not have enough strength.

My arms felt like they were about to fall off and my heart was in a million pieces. "Fine," I lied.

When I completed the turn, the rabbi took the Torah. Instant relief. Adam offered up a high five. I slapped his palm, and the congregation laughed.

Back at my row, my grandfather, in his gray suit, with his sad eyes, stepped aside to let me enter. I kissed his smooth cheek and instead of returning to my seat, walked out of the sanctuary.

In the lobby, my hands shook, but I managed to dial into my voicemail.

"Sarah woke up," Rachel's voice emanated from the phone's tiny speaker. "It's a miracle. She's awake, alert, and asking for you. A power surge, the doctor said. Come now." Rachel's voice was composed. Sarah had trained her to stay calm in any crisis. Sarah had trained me too.

Mark entered the lobby. "I'm so sorry." He enveloped me with his arms. His cologne was woodsy, masculine, the scent of safety. I wanted to hide in his embrace forever.

"Sarah didn't…She's not…" I shook my head as we split apart. "She woke from her coma. She wants to see me."

"That's great."

"But I don't have my car. I came with you."

"No worries." He handed me his keys. "Go."

I slipped on my BluBlocker sunglasses and stepped outside into the blinding sun.

Sarah's hospital floor smelled of soiled sheets and disinfectant. Her friends, clumping, filled the hallway. Everyone wore khakis, crewneck sweaters, and loafers, the unchanging wardrobe of the Happy Valley. Their hairstyles were also caught in another time. Most sported the Western Mass lesbian hairdo: cropped short, the sides layered like a bird's wings. The only exception was Connie, who still wore her hair long, despite it being more white than brown now. But their faces seemed peppier compared to last week when we'd thought Sarah's end was imminent.

"Felice." Connie embraced me. "I loved your column in the *Daily News* about buying breakfast for that homeless man."

"You read it?"

"Sarah handed out copies at my retirement party. She was so proud of you."

Not was. Is. Sarah's not dead yet, I thought.

The door to Sarah's room opened. "You made it." Rachel hugged me, then held me at arm's length. "Look at you in a suit. You've become so fashionable."

"Is Sarah still awake?" I asked.

"Yes, and she's been asking for you."

A stocky nurse in blue scrubs cut through our circle and opened the door. I moved to follow, but she stopped me and pointed to the sign: ONE VISITOR AT A TIME and barked, "Can't you read?"

"What's up with that?" I said after the nurse disappeared into Sarah's room. "Someone's dying, and they can only see one person at a time? There's not enough time for that."

"Sarah said the same thing to that nurse who gave her a speech about germs, to which Sarah replied, 'Germs are the least of my worries.'" Hearing Sarah being her sarcastic self made me smile. But only briefly.

"Is there a chance she'll fall into another coma?" I asked. Before Rachel answered me, the door reopened.

"One of you can go in now." The nurse scowled at me and returned to her station across the hall.

"Go," Rachel said. "Sarah's waiting for you."

I took a deep breath and opened the door. The fluorescent light illuminated Sarah as though she were a science experiment. She lay perfectly still, eyes closed, hair as fine as a newborn's.

Instinctively, I switched off the harsh light, then rested my hand on her leg, a slender bump beneath layers of thin cotton blankets. Sarah's blue eyes fluttered open, and a slight smile divided her chapped lips. "Blu." Her voice was barely above a whisper.

My breath caught upon hearing my pet name. I cuddled up beside her, careful not to pull out any plugs that might be keeping her alive, and placed my arm over her midsection, above the faded scar where the tumor had first set roots. "I love you, Sarah." My tears spilled onto the sterile pillowcase.

"I love you too."

A face at the door's window blurred in retreat. I reached for the lime-green privacy curtain bunched up beside the bed. One yank and the curtain moved with a metallic whizzing noise, curving around the foot of the bed and blocking the view.

"It just goes to show you," I said. "It's always something. Either you're in a coma when I visit, or the evil nurse won't let me in when you're awake."

Sarah faintly chuckled, lifting my spirits. "You always made me laugh, Blu."

"That was always my job. Even last week while you slept, I told you jokes."

"It makes me feel good to know you did that." Clouds outside separated; sunlight flooded the room. "Blu, am I going to die?"

"I didn't major in that."

Sarah smiled weakly, but her wrinkled cheeks smoothed back to serious. "Please tell me."

"Well, you always said you weren't a first timer and had past lives. Soon you'll have even more."

Sarah nodded, seeming thankful for the reminder.

"And, just to prepare you, next time you'll be Jewish," I said. Sarah's eyes widened like a child told Santa Claus isn't real. "Be thankful I prepared you with so many jokes." She grinned.

I reached into the pink plastic pitcher on the side table. "Ice chip?" I asked. Sarah nodded. I rubbed the wet crystal around her chapped lips before slipping it into her mouth, then rested my head on her chest. The familiar rhythm of her heartbeat against my cheek was comforting. Sarah placed her hand, the back of which was covered in bruises from innumerable needles, on my head. In seconds, we dozed.

"You're not supposed to get in the bed with cancer patients." Nurse Evil's bulky frame was casting a shadow over us. Sarah coughed dryly. I sat up and brought her another ice chip, but it was too large to fit in her mouth and too much effort for her to open her jaw wider, so I bit the ice and slid a sliver between Sarah's lips. She moved it around with her tongue. It clicked against the back of her teeth. I leaned down and whispered, "You're the only one in this entire hospital with a sexy woman in their bed."

Sarah gave me another smile. I was racking them up.

On my way out, I looked inside the bathroom and my heart broke. Sarah's blue-and-white toiletry bag sat unused, hygiene no longer necessary.

In the hallway, Sarah's friends were gone, most likely to the cafeteria for coffee. I ducked into a waiting room. A television on the wall showed newscasters speaking without sound. Outside, the sun began its early descent. Cars and trucks rolled by along Interstate 91. I stared into space, not ready to leave, but feeling guilty I had the choice. My stomach grumbled, but the stink of sickness killed my appetite. In the alternating din and hum of the hospital, monitors beeped, nurses shuffled by, and soda cans thumped as they landed in the machines. I was thankful Sarah had rallied so I didn't have to settle for last week's silent goodbye. These last moments spent cuddling, fingers touching, eyes meeting, made it easier to face the inevitable.

Sort of.

On an end table were pamphlets about the dangers of smoking. I picked one up and flipped it over to its blank side, then plucked a pen from a cup. I wrote SARAH in the center. From her name I drew a line and wrote LINDA. From Linda's name, I drew a line and wrote NAN. From Nan's name I drew a line and wrote CONNIE. Back at Sarah's name I added a second line and wrote FELICE. I added more lines and more names. The chart looked like the one Sarah had sketched years ago in response to my question, "How do you keep track of everyone's exes?" But I was no longer interested in keeping track of exes, only in reminding myself how few still knew the truth about me and Sarah. Sure, they might have known we had an affair, but an affair recalls something brief, fleeting, happens once and is over. Sarah and I were never over.

Walking out, I balled up the paper and tossed it into the trashcan. The hallway was quiet. I peeked through the window at Sarah's door. The bright overhead light was back on, the privacy curtain returned to its pleated position. After a quick glimpse at the empty nurses' station, I snuck in.

"I'm off to Krispy Kreme to eat a sugary doughnut in your honor." I kissed Sarah's cheek; her skin was downy soft.

"Don't forget." Sarah feebly touched her palm to my chest, the struggle to do so reflected in her features. "No matter what, I'm still there."

I choked back tears. Only after the automatic doors spit me outside into the living world could I resume breathing. I inhaled the early evening air of the Berkshires. Somewhere a fireplace burned wood.

Two days later Sarah's home number appeared on my cell phone. I was in my private office at Hunter College on the seventeenth floor, facing downtown Manhattan. I stared at the number I'd dialed daily for almost a decade. But this time, the caller must've been Katherine to tell me Sarah had passed. I was tempted to let it go to voicemail, but I'd have to deal with it eventually. I raised the phone to my ear. "Hello?"

"Blu."

"Sarah?" Never did I expect to hear her voice again, let alone over the phone. "How are you?" A ridiculous question.

"I'm home in bed with my cats. Can you visit me?" Home? The doctor had given her a day to live, two at the most, after she'd woken up from the coma, and now she was home? Did that mean she'd be okay?

"Of course." I scanned my schedule book. Meetings and events filled every hour of every day. "When?"

"We have people all week to relieve the hospice nurse." Sarah sounded energized making plans. "How about Friday? Can you come then?"

It was Monday. Would she make it till Friday?

"Sure. Can I bring you anything? Krispy Kremes?"

"Just you." Then in a calm voice, as if she were rocking on a hammock on a summer afternoon, Sarah said, "I love you."

A lump appeared in my throat. Once it subsided, I eked out, "I love you too." But it was too late. Sarah had hung up. She was gone.

Epilogue
Six Months Later

"I'm a medium," said a heavyset woman wearing a bright-blue shirt.

"That's nice," I told her. "I'm a small."

"No, really." She ignored my joke. "I'm a psychic. I talk with the dead. I've even worked with Nancy Reagan."

Great. Another New York City wing nut.

We were inside the National Arts Club in Gramercy Park. I scanned the antiquated room for someone else to talk to, but the dozens of strangers—mostly older, some famous, everyone dressed in black, except for this so-called medium—were engaged in conversations, their voices and clinking glasses reverberating off the mahogany walls. I'd just joined the Newswomen's Club of New York, and this was my first event. I looked back at the medium. Thinking it was a sign I was interested, she pressed on.

"Who did you know who had a scar from here to here?" The medium held her hands six inches apart over the lower half of her protruding stomach.

Shortly after I'd moved to the city, I'd been bilked out of $500 in a pyramid scheme. Since then, I'd remained on alert for scam artists. And this medium seemed to fit the bill. Except for that line about the scar.

I took the bait. "I had a friend with a scar there."

The medium's coral-painted lips spread into a smile. "She says she's still there, watching you."

I swallowed hard. Those were the exact words Sarah had inscribed in the last book she gave me. I wanted to respond with a snappy reply, but what would I say? Better to just walk away. I turned to leave, and she took hold of my arm, her fingers pinching the skin. I glanced around to see if anyone noticed our exchange, maybe would come to my rescue, but everyone continued drinking wine and nibbling cheese.

"Was her name Sally?" the medium asked. A tightening filled my chest. Tears pooled behind my eyes. How had she come up with Sarah's childhood nickname?

"How did you?" I stared into her eyes, brown with yellow flecks. The sound in the room faded away, replaced by a ringing in my ears. Was it possible to connect to our dead loved ones?

"I told you. I'm a medium."

A waiter walked by with a tray of wineglasses. With a trembling hand, I grabbed a glass, downed the wine, and gagged. A mix of sadness, joy, and fear funneled through me.

The medium, still clutching my arm, smiled; she'd bagged another believer. "I'm sorry if I made you upset. I just wanted to pass along your friend's message." She released my arm and stepped away; blue swallowed into a sea of blackness. I wanted to run after her, have her touch me again, as though connecting to her connected me to Sarah.

"Are you okay?" A woman in a dark pantsuit appeared. "You look very pale."

"That woman was a medium." I nodded in the direction she went. "And she just said the name of my dead ex."

"Did she say Michael or John?" The woman said dismissively. "Because those names are common."

"No." I shook my head. "She said Sally."

That night I dreamt that Sarah was sitting on a chair in my room. I got out of bed and sat on her lap. "What are you doing here? We told everyone you died." Sarah put her hand to my cheek, but before she could respond I woke up. Grabbing my journal from the nightstand, I wrote a dozen pages without stopping, all about saying goodbye to the first love of my life who was dying of cancer.

On a whim, I entered those pages in the Bronx Recognizes Its Own First Chapter Writing Contest. And won. The reward was a generous stipend and a reading at a New York City library. Mom had surprised me and driven down from Massachusetts. As I came to the podium to read, I saw her in the front row with Uncle Mark. Already I was scared to read this material, which made me feel vulnerable, in front of strangers. Now I worried about her reaction, too. Would she be shocked? Disappointed?

When I finished, Mom came up to me with tears in her eyes. "I wish you'd told me what you'd been going through so I could've been there for you." As we hugged, stillness came over me. All those years I'd spent agonizing over what she would think: they were gone in an instant. Her acceptance marked the beginning of my own, although I still had a lot of work to do.

"Excuse me," said a middle-aged man wearing a tan sport coat. "I'm a literary agent. How much of the book do you have completed?"

What book?

He handed me his business card. "Call me when it's finished."

But it would be a long time before I finished this book. Not because of the writing process itself, but because of the healing one. Each rewrite proved to be a private visit with Sarah—one I didn't want to end. Her absence left a hole inside me that felt like a winter Sunday afternoon: cold, desolate, and lonely. I spent years trying to fill that hole with brief affairs, both with men and women, despite still being with Erin. Each dalliance temporarily satisfied that void, recaptured some small part of the special feeling I'd had with Sarah. At least at first. When the other person started to ask more of the relationship, I'd end it. The affairs were an attempt to return to a place I remembered being happy. I was confusing secretiveness with love.

"Secrets are also tied to shame," said my Upper East Side therapist. We were sitting in her Fifth Avenue office overlooking Central Park. "And when you feel shame about a secret, you're more apt to keep it hidden."

I was still doing this. No one knew Sarah and I had still been together when she'd died. I mourned Sarah exactly as I'd loved her: in secret. I went through the five stages of grief in silence, getting stuck on the second: anger.

I was angry at Sarah for leaving me and for taking the house away. Angry at myself for letting my fear of what people thought keep me from being with the person I'd loved. And angry at the world for not automatically accepting couples like Sarah and me. Erin bore the brunt of my pain and frustration, which came in the form of my unpredictable mood swings. I wanted to share with her my feelings, but I couldn't explain my sadness without telling her my secret, and I couldn't tell her my secret without explaining I'd still been in love with Sarah as Erin and I had been dating. Anything I said would've hurt her, and I was already hurting her enough.

A rift grew between us. Erin tried for seven years to mend it with couples therapy, self-help books, and months-long breaks, but our relationship couldn't be fixed. A relationship required both sides to be fully invested.

By my late thirties, despite my imploding love life, my career had kicked into another gear. I was a weekly opinion columnist at a New York City newspaper, an author, a motivational speaker, a Holocaust educator. I even bought my own apartment. But regardless of all the adulting I was doing, I was still making relationship decisions based on where I'd been emotionally at twenty-three, subconsciously seeking out unavailable partners.

I left Hunter and started working at another City University of New York school. On my first day, I met Robert who was kind, handsome, and eleven years older. He had a full head of salt-and-pepper hair, was separated from his wife, and had two little kids, which meant he could only offer half of himself. I jumped.

Robert's passion was fine woodworking. I loved watching him turn planks of wood into beautiful pieces of furniture while I swept up sawdust and organized his tools. We were good together. We went for long bicycle rides and slept holding hands. In fact, we held hands everywhere we went: Home Depot, Trader Joe's, even walking down Commercial Street in Provincetown. With him I felt a comfort I'd spent years searching for.

Two years in, his divorce finalized, we maintained separate lives because he had his kids every other weekend and they never knew about me. I accepted this arrangement because I was aware how important a father-child connection was, but also because I felt comfortable in that familiar pact: we were secretly dating at work, spending one or two days a week together, and I would not call him when his kids were around. After several years, I did ask Robert to spend a weekend with him and his children, but he said no because we weren't married, which he otherwise wanted. However, marriage was the ultimate "all in" and I wasn't trained for that. Both of us made ultimatums, and both of us were unwilling to budge. After nine years, Robert and I were over. Friends asked if I was okay. But the benefits to being half in was that it kept your heart from getting hurt. Also, I had someone waiting in the wings. Habits are hard to break.

A month later, while visiting my parents on Cape Cod, a pipe burst in the basement, drenching a storage room. Whatever could be salvaged was spread out on the lawn to dry. In a box of my old keepsakes, I found a letter I'd written to Sarah the morning after we'd been caught by Linda.

> May 8, 1994
>
> Dear Sarah,
>
> Does this mean we can become a real couple? It's what my heart wants, but my heart isn't the half in charge. My brain calls the shots and it's keeping me from admitting how loving you and being loved by you makes me feel happy, special, warm, and safe. Mark says I should do what feels right, but I don't know any more what right feels like. He asked me if I would want to live with you if Linda left, and I said no, but that was simply reflex. I do want to live with you, I just don't know how. Barbara says the only way I'll ever be happy is to stop hiding behind our secret. I guess that means I'm doomed to a lifetime of unhappiness. Ironic since my name means happy. ♥Blu

I looked up from the letter, speechless. Dad always said the solution to any problem was most often found within the problem itself. He was right. Staring back at me was the answer to my chronic inability to commit fully to a new relationship: I had to stop hiding my past. Of course, I'd had the solution the whole time, I just hadn't been ready to take the leap. Now I was.

For years I thought my fear stemmed from what others would think if they knew I'd been in love with a much older woman. I'd been mistaken. The real fear was examining what I had thought about myself. I'd been judging myself harshly for loving someone society deemed an unacceptable match and had been anticipating that same judgement from others. Secrecy enabled me to compartmentalize this fear, which then intensified my shame. My heightened shame then kept me silent and kept me fearful. It was a vicious cycle.

But not anymore.

Writing my story has helped me get the angst off my chest and the spinning thoughts out of my head. But it wasn't enough. Releasing the book was like cleaning out the clutter in my heart and mind, and making room to fall in love—to let love in again. Sarah, despite her faults, taught me how to do that. I don't regret our affair, nor do I blame Sarah for the path my life has taken. She was never the villain in my story. Yes, Sarah was fallible, I see that now: she cheated on Linda with a young, impressionable woman. But that's not the takeaway I choose. As heavy as my heart was, it was being used for what hearts are intended to do: love.

When I think about Sarah now, it's the good memories that return. I've come to appreciate how precious they are, exactly what Sarah had tried to pass on to me almost thirty years ago when she'd said, "Having memories are better than not having them." And I have them in spades. What I don't have, for the first time since I was twenty-three, is a partner. It's quite liberating. I'm free of secrets. When I start dating again, I'll be doing so from a clean slate. A first.

I've finally come to accept that loving Sarah hadn't been wrong; it was the act of loving her in secret. If I could go back and be with Sarah publicly, and give my friends and family the opportunity to accept us instead of having decided for them, I would. But I can't. What I can do, which is almost as good, is tell my story. Am I scared? A little, but I can hear Sarah telling me it's time.

"Our time."

Acknowledgements

Writing this book has been a labor of love and I could not have done it without the support of so many. Over the years I have worked with several editors, each one contributing exactly what I needed at the time. Thank you to Erin Brown, Rebecca Faith Heyman, Deb Stead, Margaret Diehl, Debra Englander, Sophia Dembling, and Sarah Cypher for your extraordinary editorial help.

I am especially grateful to Ellen Roberts at Where Books Begin for helping me, well, begin this book. When you said, "You've got something here," I believed you. And to Lesléa Newman, thank you for helping me turn those beginning words into a story. Your friendship over the years has meant so much. Thank you also to Janice Obuchowski, my last editor. I will forever be indebted to you for pushing me right out of my comfort zone.

Thank you to Keri-Rae Barnum at New Shelves Books for your patience with all my questions. (And there were many.) Your answers were, and continue to be, invaluable. To Miladinka Milic, talented cover designer extraordinaire. Thank you for saving the day. You really are, as your name means, a miracle.

To Ann Reed, thank you for your music. Your songs and lyrics had a little part in bringing Sarah and me together. They've also helped me heal.

Thank you to Rita Mae Brown. Your poetry was the impetus for the love I got to experience. Your support and encouragement mean the world to me. Having you in my corner makes me feel like saying, "Pinch me." Dreams really do come true.

My deep gratitude to the many friends (some of whom I've known since nursery school) who read this book in its numerous versions, made helpful suggestions, and gave me encouragement: Alicia Mathewson, Cheryl Kerrigan, Lauren Lindsay, Natalie Caine, Susan Zimmer, Julie Trainito, Elizabeth Gesualdo, T.W., Jody (Stringer) Scott, Jay Boyne, and Sau Man Kam. Special thanks to Tere Mele for your continuous support and for reading the book six times!

Thank you to my Aunt Marcia Boland Wells for your honest and gracious feedback. To my Uncle Mark Schwartzbaum, who read an earlier draft in one sitting. Every time you laughed out loud it made my heart sing. To my sisters Jackie Cohen Burkey and Meredith Cohen, thank you for your endless compassion. How lucky am I to have the most supportive sisters ever. Of course, you had a good role model.

Lastly, to my parents, Shelly and Richard Cohen. Mom, I know this was not an easy book for you to read, and that you only wanted to keep me from getting hurt. I appreciate your protectiveness. Your comments about my hair? Not so much. (Just kidding.) Dad, thank you for your perceptive edits, keen insights, and endless praise. I hit the jackpot parent lottery.

About the Author

Felice Cohen, known nationally and internationally as the woman who lived in one of the world's smallest apartments, is an author, speaker and Holocaust educator. Her book *90 Lessons for Living Large in 90 Square Feet (...or More)*, the recipient of numerous Self Help book awards, was inspired by the YouTube video of her 90-square-foot New York City studio that went viral with tens of millions of views, gaining media attention across the globe. Felice was able to "live large" in that tiny studio because she's been organizing closets since she could walk. As the grandchild of two Holocaust survivors, Felice is also the author of *What Papa Told Me*, a memoir about her grandfather's life before, during and after the war. The book has sold around the world, been endorsed by Elie Wiesel and Yad Vashem in Israel, is taught in schools across the country, and has been translated into Polish. She splits her time between New York City and Cape Cod, Massachusetts.

Connect with Felice on Social Media

Website: https://www.felicecohen.com
Twitter: @FeliceCohen
Facebook: felicecohenauthor
Instagram: FeliceCohen90
TikTok: @FeliceCohen90
LinkedIn: Felice-Cohen

Thanks for reading!

Thank you for purchasing this book. If you enjoyed reading *Half In*, please consider sharing this book with your friends by posting to Facebook, Twitter, Instagram, TikTok, or painting a sign and sticking it in your front yard. I'd also be thankful if you'd consider writing a review on Amazon, Goodreads, Bookbub, or wherever you hang out online.

If you're interested in receiving my newsletter, notifications of new releases, or special offers on my books, please join my email list by going to my website: www.felicecohen.com. Your feedback and support mean so much.

Thank you and happy reading.

WOFTOG!

Felice

In Loving Memory

Made in the USA
Middletown, DE
02 February 2023